A FIRST BIOLOGY COURSE

36.

36/40

Also from Stanley Thornes (Publishers) Ltd
A FIRST CHEMISTRY COURSE by E N Ramsden

A FIRST BIOLOGY COURSE

P T Bunyan BSc MIBiol

Roade Comprehensive School, Northants

Stanley Thornes (Publishers) Ltd

First published in 1982 by Stanley Thornes (Publishers) Ltd, Educa House, Old Station Drive, off Leckhampton Road, Cheltenham GL53 0DN

Reprinted 1982

British Library Cataloguing in Publication Data
     Bunyan, Philip T.
          A first course in biology.
          1. Biology
          I. Title
          574   QH308.7

          ISBN 0–85950–339–9

Phototypeset by Promenade Graphics Ltd, Cheltenham
Printed in Great Britain at The Pitman Press, Bath

Contents

Preface

This book has been written as an introductory text for those who have not studied Biology before. Its most obvious niche is in the first two to three years of secondary education where it can be used by pupils studying Biology or as a part of a general science course. It may be equally useful in middle and primary schools.

With this in mind, I have tried to make the language simple and avoid potentially unintelligible jargon. Scientific terms, however, are necessary and each time one appears it has been explained as simply as possible.

The book is designed to be read by the pupils themseves. In each chapter the sections build on previous ones, gradually presenting as wide a picture as possible. However, as an introduction the amount of information is necessarily limited, allowing the teacher to expand and extend if he wishes.

I have included a large number of experiments because any science is learned most easily by discovery. Each experiment has a clear set of instructions, separated from the rest of the text, and many also include a question at the end to guide the pupil towards formulating his or her own conclusion. Many of the experiments are simple and can be performed equally well with pieces of equipment available in most households. Demonstration experiments will normally be done by the teacher.

P T BUNYAN
Towcester 1982

Acknowledgements

I would like to thank the following, who have kindly supplied photographs for inclusion in this book:

B & B Photographs, for Figure 3.2(c), which shows parenchyma cells, and Figure 10.15

BBC Hulton Picture Library, for Figures 3.1, 4.6, 4.16 and 4.17

Dr Betty Brownell of the Department of Neuropathology, Frenchay Hospital, Bristol, for Figure 3.2(b), which shows motor neurones from the brain, in a histological section

Bruce Coleman Ltd., for Figure 3.2(a), which shows human blood cells, and Figure 6.6.

I am also grateful to the following for permission to adapt their artwork:

British Dental Association, for illustrations in *Yours For Life* adapted for Figures 7.14 and 7.15

Oxford University Press, for an illustration from *A Modern Introduction to Biology* by B S Beckett adapted for Figure 10.16.

I would like to acknowledge the considerable help I have had from the following people during the preparation of this book: Mr Mel Davis and Mr Don Manley, for their help with the crosswords and wordfinders; Mr Stewart Cook, for reading and criticising the original draft; Stanley Thornes (Publishers), for their assistance and advice at each stage of production; and finally my wife, Terry, for typing the manuscript, criticising my English, and for her moral support and infinite patience.

P T BUNYAN

1. Beginning Biology

1.1 What is Biology?

Scientists are people who try to understand the world we live in. They *observe* the world to see what is going on in it. By thinking about what they observe, scientists may be able to see patterns and relationships which help them to understand more fully why things are the way they are. Scientists can use this information to help them improve life for us.

Biology is the science of living things. A *biologist* tries to find out more about how animals and plants work. Biologists like to know more about what goes on inside you, and inside other animals and plants too. Biology is concerned also with why there are so many different sorts of plants and animals; why some of them are so big and some so small; what gives some plants such beautiful flowers; and why some animals should have such bright colours or such shapes.

All these animals and plants live together. Some animals eat plants and some eat other animals, and yet very few seem to become extinct. Why is this? To a biologist, the world is full of questions just waiting to be answered. No one person can answer all of them and many just study one or two animals or plants. Scientists share their information by writing books and by talking to each other.

Biologists, like any other scientists, will ask questions about what they see. They may do an *experiment* to try and answer those questions. Often they may need special equipment to do their experiments. This equipment is called *apparatus*, and the special room where the scientist may work is called a *laboratory* (or *lab* for short). Of course to a biologist, any place where plants and animals live can be a lab, but often we need to bring things indoors so that we can look more closely at them.

Suppose a scientist has asked the question 'What do worms eat?' He could spend many days and nights sitting in a field trying to find the answer, but this may not be the best way of working. To help himself, the scientist will make a careful guess at the answer. He could, for example, say 'Worms eat small insects'. This guess or suggestion is called a *hypothesis*, and he will then go on to plan and do an experiment to see if his hypothesis was right. Another

1

hypothesis could have been 'Worms eat dead leaves'. For each hypothesis the scientist must do an experiment until he is satisfied that he has the right answer.

Remember, not all hypotheses will be right; the experiment may prove them to be wrong. Wrong hypotheses are rejected and new ones tried.

1.2 Working in a laboratory

You will be working in a lab and there are some rules which you must follow if you are to work safely and successfully.

Lab rules

1. Work quietly on your own experiment. Do not touch anything that is not part of your experiment. Move quietly and steadily around the lab. Do not run.

2. Follow the instructions carefully. If you are not sure, then check with the teacher. Do not do any experiments that you have invented yourself unless you first check with your teacher.

3. Do not taste anything at all and never drink the water from the taps.

4. Be clean and tidy. Use clean apparatus and clean up after you have finished. Do not throw solid wastes down the sink but put them into bins. Work like a proper scientist should.

5. Tell your teacher immediately of any accidents, cuts, burns or splashes.

1.3 What is a living organism?

You are a *living organism*. Anything which is alive is called a living organism. The question is 'How do we know when something is alive?' We often try to test if an animal is alive by prodding it. If it moves away, then it is alive. Not all living organisms move. For instance, we could prod a tree all day and it would not move. In

2

fact, we would be quite surprised if it did. But trees are alive; we talk about live trees or dead trees, and just by looking we are able to see which are alive.

The best way of telling if a thing is alive is by asking the question 'Has it grown or is it growing?' By 'growing' we usually mean 'getting bigger', and all living organisms grow. We can, however, grow crystals; does this mean that the crystal is alive? No, of course not, but there must be some other way of telling if a thing is alive. We ask the question 'Can it *reproduce*?' By 'reproduce' we mean 'can it, or can a pair of them, produce seeds, or eggs or something which will grow into a new living organism?' Crystals cannot do that.

Living organisms use *energy* to grow and reproduce. They get this energy from chemicals in a similar way to how we get heat energy by burning a piece of coal. This 'getting energy' is called *respiration*. Unfortunately we cannot usually see living organisms respiring but we can test for it in other ways. Crystals do not respire, either.

The area that an organism lives in is called its *environment*; it includes all the living and non-living things which surround it and may have some effect on the way that it lives. Your environment includes your home and your school, the town where you live and all the people and plants and animals in it. You, in your turn, are part of lots of other organisms' environments.

Often the environment may change, and this may make it better or worse for living in. Living organisms are aware of the changes, some more than others, and they may do something to take advantage of good changes or to get away from bad ones. This is called *responding* to the environment.

If it starts raining, you will be aware of this change for the worse and you will respond by taking shelter. Some flowers respond by closing up until the rain stops (see Figure 1.1 over the page). What would a crystal do?

You must remember that not all organisms can detect all the changes going on around them. Many very tiny living things can detect only a few, since lots of them live in water where there are not so many changes. Even you cannot detect everything. For example, there are changes in radio waves which your radio can detect but you cannot, but this has no effect on how you live.

3

Figure 1.1 Responding to the environment

All living organisms can detect some changes and all can do something about some of them. Our crystal cannot detect anything.

What then is a living organism? It is something which can grow and reproduce. It also respires. It can detect some changes in its environment and can respond to them. Some living organisms can move.

1. Choose from the list below all the living organisms:

Man, chalk, mouse, stickleback, oil, oak table, buttercup, oak tree, willow cricket bat, fly, stalagmite, tortoise, volcano, butterfly, frog, cotton shirt, vegetable rack, grass, woollen jumper, blackbird, apple tree

2. Copy out the chart and for each living organism write down how it reproduces, whether it lays eggs or makes seeds or just has babies.

Organism	How it reproduces

1.4 Looking at living organisms

If you look around you, you will see many different living organisms. You can see other people, trees, flowers, dogs, cats and many more. Some organisms are quite a lot like each other and some are very different. When we look at them all it would help us to understand them if we could put them into groups which have things in common.

There are two easy groups to recognise. The animals and the plants. What is the difference between an animal and a plant? Well, to start with, most animals move from place to place and plants do not. Most plants have got leaves of some sort, which are green. They use these leaves to catch the Sun's energy, which they need to help them grow. This is the main difference. Plants can use the Sun's energy and animals cannot. Some animals eat plants for energy and they themselves may get eaten by other animals. And so it goes on. Plants trap the energy, and animals eat to get energy.

Identifying some animals and plants

1. Copy out the chart below.

Animal or plant	How to identify it

2. Write down the name of five animals and five plants that you know.

3. For each animal and plant write down in the second column the features which are special to that animal or plant and help you to recognise it.

In your list you might have written down 'Fly'. You could recognise a fly because it has wings and flies. It is not like a bird because it is small and has no feathers. You could also have written down 'Daffodil'. You can recognise this because it is tall with big yellow flowers and not small with small flowers like a buttercup.

1.5 Using keys

What do we do about plants and animals we cannot recognise? These can be recognised using a key which is a series of questions which we ask. Each answer takes us on to another question, and so on until we arrive at the name of the organism. Here is a simple key to identify lab apparatus for you to try in the lab to show you how they work.

Experiment 1.1

Using a simple key

1. Start at Question 1.

2. For each answer you will only have to say yes or no.

3. After each yes or no there may be another question number. This is the question you must go to next. Sometimes there will not be another question number; there will be a name. This is the name of the piece of apparatus.

4. When you have identified each piece of apparatus, make a neat pencil drawing of it and label it with its name. This will also help you to learn the apparatus.

Question 1.   Is it made of glass?

      Answer: Yes.   Go to Question 2.
              No.   Go to Question 5.

Question 2.   Is it tall and thin?

      Answer: Yes.   Go to Question 3.
              No.   Go to Question 4.

Question 3.   Does it have lines and numbers on the side?

      Answer: Yes.   It is a measuring cylinder.
              No.   It is a test-tube.

Question 4.   Is it shaped like a cone?

      Answer: Yes.   It is a conical flask.
              No.   It is a beaker.

Question 5.   Is it made of wood?

      Answer: Yes.   Go to Question 6.
              No.   Go to Question 7.

Question 6.   Is it a thin piece of wood?

      Answer: Yes.   It is a splint.
              No.   It is a test-tube rack.

Question 7.   Is it like a pair of scissors?

      Answer: Yes.   It is a pair of tongs.
              No.   It is a spatula.

The next step is to use a key to identify some animals found among dead leaves and twigs known as *leaf litter*. These animals will all be small and belong to the group known as *invertebrates*, because they have no backbone. Invertebrates include insects, spiders, snails, slugs, worms, crabs, and many other animals. They are usually small and do not have a skeleton inside like humans do. This means they are soft and bendy like a worm, and because of this some of them make hard shells to live in. Some of them, like the insects and spiders, have a very thin but strong outside covering called an *exoskeleton*. This means that they can have legs and wings and jaws as well as protection for their bodies. They can move around much more easily and quickly on land than invertebrates that do not have an exoskeleton.

The other major group of animals are the *vertebrates*. These have a backbone as part of a skeleton inside their bodies, called an *endoskeleton*. Man is a vertebrate, and so are birds, fish, snakes and lizards, frogs, and many more. We will look more closely at vertebrates later.

Insects

Many of the animals you will see are insects. There are hundreds of different sorts and to be able to identify them you must learn a little about them. All insects have six legs. Their bodies are divided into three parts although it is not always easy to see these. The *head* carries the mouth parts, which may be biting structures or may be drawn out into long tubes for sucking plant or animal juices. There are two large eyes and a pair of feelers called *antennae*. The *thorax* is only three segments and the six legs are attached to these. The *abdomen* is the rest of the insect. It is made of a number of segments, but sometimes these are covered, or partly covered by wings or wing cases. Figure 1.2 shows two different insects: a ground beetle, which has the abdomen covered by wing cases; and an ant, which does not.

Young insects are called *larvae* and may sometimes look very different to the adult. For instance, a young butterfly is called a 'caterpillar' and looks nothing like a butterfly. Insects and their larvae can be very hard to identify.

To look at small organisms you will need to use a hand lens, or magnifying glass, which will magnify eight or ten times. To use this correctly, hold the lens close to the object you are looking at. Then move the lens towards your eye until the object comes into focus (Figure 1.3).

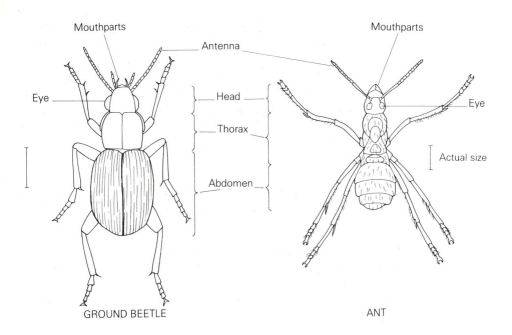

Mouthparts

Antenna

Eye

Head

Thorax

Abdomen

GROUND BEETLE

Mouthparts

Eye

Actual size

ANT

Figure 1.2   The parts of insects

Move the hand lens
this way until
the object is in
focus

Figure 1.3   How to use a hand lens

Looking at the animals in leaf litter

1.   Put your leaf litter on to a sheet of newspaper.

2.   Thoroughly sort through the material with a paint brush or pencil. Carefully remove any animals and put them into a Petri dish or a beaker with a cardboard lid.

3.   Identify as many of the animals as possible using the key. You must realise, however, that there are hundreds of different animals that you could find. The key will allow you to identify the most common types but you may need a book from the library to identify them all. Figure 1.4 contains drawings of some of the most common animals.

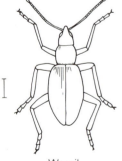

Ground beetle

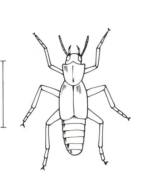

Rove beetle

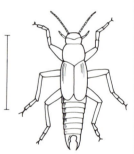

Earwig

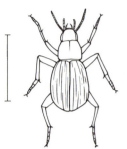

Weevil

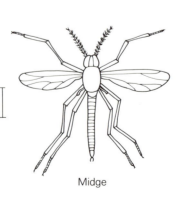

Midge

Midge

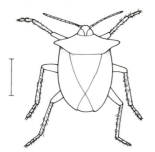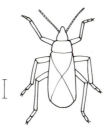

Plant bugs

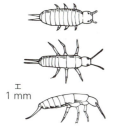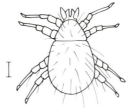

1 mm

Springtails

Mite

Centipede

Spider

Snail

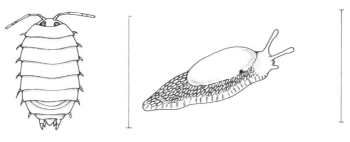

Woodlouse

Slug

Millipede

Figure 1.4 (continued on p. 12)

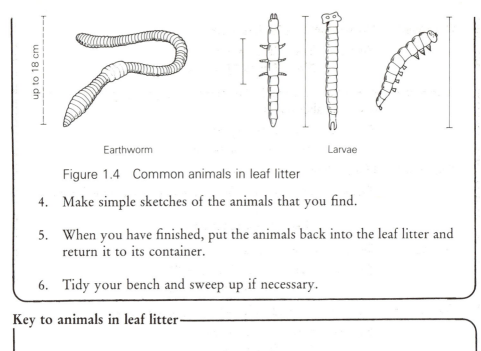

Earthworm   Larvae

up to 18 cm

Figure 1.4   Common animals in leaf litter

4. Make simple sketches of the animals that you find.

5. When you have finished, put the animals back into the leaf litter and return it to its container.

6. Tidy your bench and sweep up if necessary.

Key to animals in leaf litter

Question 1. Does it have legs?

        Answer: Yes.   Go to Question 2.
                  No.   Go to Question 14.

Question 2. Does it have six legs?

        Answer: Yes.   Go to Question 3.
                  No.   Go to Question 10.

Question 3. Is its body divided into segments more or less the same size?

        Answer: Yes.   It is a larva of some sort.
                  No.   Go to Question 4.

Question 4. Does it have hard wing cases?

        Answer: Yes.   Go to Question 5.
                  No.   Go to Question 7.

Question 5. Does it have a pointed nose with its antennae at the end?

        Answer: Yes.   It is a weevil.
                  No.   Go to Question 6.

Question 6. Does it have pincers on the end of its abdomen?

        Answer: Yes.   It is an earwig.
                  No.   It is some other sort of beetle.

Question 7.   Does it have a pinched waist?

        Answer: Yes.   It is an ant.
                  No.   Go to Question 8.

Question 8.   Is it between 1 and 2 mm long with a springing fork tucked under its abdomen?

        Answer: Yes.   It is a springtail.
                  No.   Go to Question 9.

Question 9.   Does it have only two wings?

        Answer: Yes.   It is a fly of some sort or a midge or a gnat.
                  No.   It is a plant bug.

Question 10.   Does it have eight legs?

        Answer: Yes.   Go to Question 11.
                  No.   Go to Question 12.

Question 11.   Is its body clearly divided into two sections?

        Answer: Yes.   It is a spider.
                  No.   It is a mite.

Question 12.   Is it long and thin with lots of segments?

        Answer: Yes.   Go to Question 13.
                  No.   It is a woodlouse.

Question 13.   Does it have two legs per segment?

        Answer: Yes.   It is a centipede.
                  No.   It is a millipede.

Question 14.   Does it have a shell?

        Answer: Yes.   It is a snail.
                  No.   Go to Question 15.

Question 15.   Is its body divided into segments?

        Answer: Yes.   Go to Question 16.
                  No.   It is a slug.

Question 16.   Is it fairly long and worm-like with tiny bristles on its underside?

        Answer: Yes.   It is a worm.
                  No.   It is a larva of some sort, e.g. a maggot or a leatherjacket.

1.6 Vertebrates

Vertebrates are animals which have a backbone. Having a backbone and a well-developed skeleton has meant that vertebrates could grow much larger than invertebrates and become much more visible.

Vertebrates are not more important than invertebrates. However, being big, we notice them more and of course many of them are directly useful to us. They provide us with meat, milk, eggs and materials for clothes and, in days gone by, the horses and oxen provided the only means of transport and the power to pull farm machines.

Some vertebrates are known as *warm-blooded*. This is not strictly accurate since many so called cold-blooded animals can have warm blood too. Warm-blooded animals can keep their body temperature constant all the time even when it is very cold or very hot. This means that they can work efficiently all the time. *Cold-blooded* animals are usually the same temperature as their surroundings, and therefore if it is cold they do not work so well. Being at the same fairly high temperature all the time is a distinct advantage and is one of the reasons why man has been so successful.

The five groups of vertebrates are: *mammals, birds, reptiles, amphibians* and *fish*.

Mammals   Mammals have hair on their bodies. They give birth to living babies which are fed on milk from their mothers. They are warm-blooded.

Birds   Birds have feathers and can usually fly. They lay eggs from which their young hatch. They too are warm-blooded.

Reptiles   Reptiles can live both in and out of water but they lay their eggs on land. They have scales and are cold-blooded.

Amphibians   Amphibians can live both in land and in water. Their young hatch from eggs laid in water and are called tadpoles. These live in water only. They are cold-blooded.

Fish   Fish live in water and breathe using gills. They have scales, not feathers or hair, and are cold-blooded.

Write a list of five animals from each of the groups of vertebrates. For each animal give one reason why it belongs to the group you have chosen.

1.7 The microscope

Many animals and plants, or parts of them, are too small even to be seen with a hand lens. To study them you need a microscope. This is a very useful piece of apparatus which must be treated with great care since it is easily damaged. You must learn about the microscope if you are to use it correctly.

The microscope has two different *lenses*. The *eyepiece* lens is the part you look through and the *objective* lens is the part nearest the *specimen*. Your microscope may have two or three different objective lenses which can be twisted into position to change the magnification. The total magnification of the microscope is the magnification of the eyepiece lens multiplied by the magnification of the objective lens, e.g.

$$\left(\begin{array}{c} \text{Eyepiece lens} \\ \times\ 10 \end{array} \right) \times \left(\begin{array}{c} \text{Objective lens} \\ \times\ 10 \end{array} \right) = \left(\begin{array}{c} \text{Total} \\ \text{magnification} \\ \times\ 100 \end{array} \right)$$

Using these lenses what you are looking at will seem 100 times as long as it really is and 100 times as wide.

Your specimen is put on to a thin piece of glass called a *microscope slide*, and this is placed on the *stage*. There is a hole in the centre of the stage; light reflects off the *mirror*, through the specimen and up through the lenses to your eye. If you use a too-thick specimen, no light will pass through it and you will see only darkness. The microscope is *focused* by the *adjustment knob* which, depending on your microscope, may move the lenses or the stage. The *body* is the part which supports the lenses and the stage and when moving a microscope it must *always* be picked up by the body.

Now check with your microscope that you can identify all the main parts (see Figure 1.5 over the page).

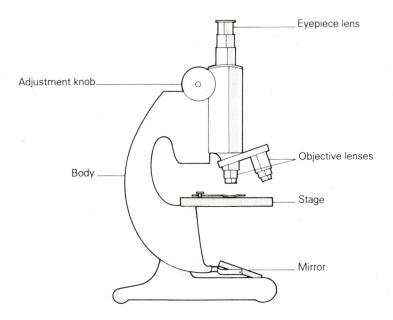

Figure 1.5   The parts of a microscope

How to use a microscope

1. Set up the microscope so that the low-power objective lens is in position.

2. Look down the microscope and arrange the mirror so that light is reflected from a window or a lamp (but never direct sunlight) up into the microscope.

3. Place your specimen so that it is in the centre of the hole in the stage.

4. While looking from the side of the microscope turn the adjustment knob so that the objective lens and the specimen are close to each other.

5. Now look down the microscope and move the lens away from the specimen until it comes into clear focus. Try to keep both eyes open whilst you do this. Never focus by bringing the lens and the specimen together because you may miss the correct focus and push the lens through the slide.

1.8 Pond organisms

A drop of water from a pond or river may contain hundreds of tiny animals and plants. You can easily see them with the microscope using the low-power lens. Some of them move very quickly and you may have to move the slide about to follow them. These organisms are very different from the animals and plants we see normally, but they form a very important part of pond life. They form the food of a lot of small fish which in turn are eaten by larger fish. So you can see that without them our pond life would be very different.

There are many different sorts of pond organisms, and you may have difficulty in using a key to identify them. Instead Figure 1.6 contains pictures of the most common ones and you should use these for identification.

Amoeba

Paramecium
(Slipper animal)

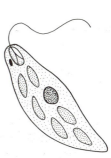

Euglena

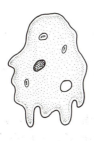

A flagellate

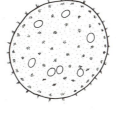

Volvox

Vorticella

Figure 1.6 (continued on p. 18)

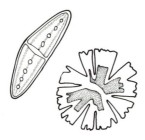

Desmids

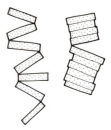

Diatoms

Spirogyra

Cyclops

Daphnia (Water flea)

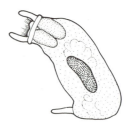

Rotifer (Wheel animal)

Figure 1.6   Common pond organisms

Experiment 1.3

Looking at pond organisms

1. Set up your microscope with the low-power lens.

2. Take a drop of water in a pipette and place it on a clean slide.

3. Being careful not to spill any water, put the slide on to the microscope stage.

4. Focus the organisms and identify as many as you can.

5. Make clear drawings of some of the organisms you see.

6. Repeat the experiment with water from other ponds or streams.

7. Clear up, making sure both the microscope and slide are clean and dry.

Questions on Chapter 1

1. Write down the correct words to fill in the blanks in these sentences:
   (a) An organism is alive if it _____ and _____ and respires.
   (b) The _____ is the area an organism lives in and the plants and animals in it.
   (c) Plants can use the _____ energy but animals cannot. Animals get their energy by _____ plants.
   (d) An _____ has six legs, but a _____ has eight.
   (e) Animals without a backbone are called _____, and animals with a backbone are _____.

2. Make up a key to identify eight different objects commonly found in a kitchen.

3. Find out the difference between the leaves of six trees. Make up a key to identify them.

4. Explain the differences between the five groups of vertebrates.

Crossword on Chapter 1

Across

1 Middle part of an insect's body (6)
3 It gets its 8 across from the Sun (5)
8 Animals get it from the food they eat (6)
9 A type of insect, like the ladybird (6)
12 The areas organisms live in (12)
14 A bird hatches out of this (3)
16 All living organisms do this (7)
19 A female sheep (3)
20 Animals at the zoo (4)
21 When something grows older it increases its _____ (3)
22 Animals do this but plants do not (4)
23 An instrument for looking at small things (10)

Down

1 A very large plant (4)
2 See 11 down
4 Dead leaves and twigs are often called leaf _____ (6)
5 and 10. All animals have _____ to live, but plants do not (2, 3)
6 An animal with a backbone (10)
7 The rear section of an insect's body (7)
10 See 5 down
11 and 2. A cat is a _____ (6, 8)
13 Biology and Physics are examples of this (7)
15 Most plants are this colour (5)
17 Gets bigger (5)
18 An insect which makes honey (3)
21 Upper limb on the human body (3)

Trace this grid on to a piece of paper, and then fill in the answers.

2. Living organisms in action

2.1 What do living organisms do?

You now know that a living organism grows and reproduces. It respires, can detect some changes in its environment, and can respond to them. It may move. We must now look at one or two organisms to see how they go about doing these things. We may not be able to find out everything about the organism, but by asking some questions and trying to find the answers we will begin to understand questions like 'what does it look like?', 'what is it doing?', 'where does it live?'

You must realise that there are thousands and thousands of different living organisms, which do not all work in the same way. We cannot look at all of them, but only one or two, so the answers we get may not apply to other organisms. Our answers will, however, help us to ask the right questions when we look at other organisms.

2.2 The earthworm, a common organism

You can all recognise the common worm. You may have dug some up in your garden, or seen a thrush pulling one out of the ground. In fact there are four different sorts of worm common in this country, and they are all slightly different.

The one we will look at is the common earthworm which has the scientific name *Lumbricus terrestris*. This is shown in Figure 2.1.

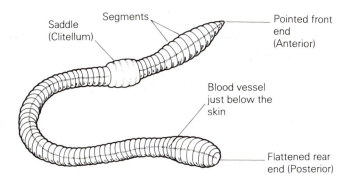

Figure 2.1   The common earthworm (*Lumbricus terrestris*)

Estimating worm numbers

1. Measure an area of ground 1 m × 1 m square.

2. Mark out the area with string or four 1 m rules (see Figure 2.3).

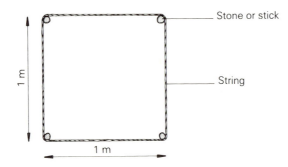

Figure 2.3   An area for estimating worm numbers

3. Count the number of worm casts in this area.

4. Now choose a different area, perhaps a spot under a tree or hedge. Do the experiment again.

5. Fill your results in a chart like the one below.

Brief description of area	Number of casts

6. You can repeat the experiment for as many different habitats as you can find. Read the opening passage of this section again before you write the conclusion to this experiment.

In your experiment, did you find a difference in the number of casts in the different areas? What do you think could have caused this? Try to think about the soil. Was it wet or dry? Was it sandy or like clay? What sorts of plants grew in the soil? Did they shade it? Did they provide leaves for the worms to eat, because worms come out of their burrows at night and collect fallen leaves and pull them into their burrows? (See Figure 2.4.)

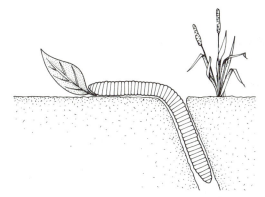

Figure 2.4   A worm dragging a fallen leaf back into its burrow

Experiment 2.4

Looking at where worms live—the wormery

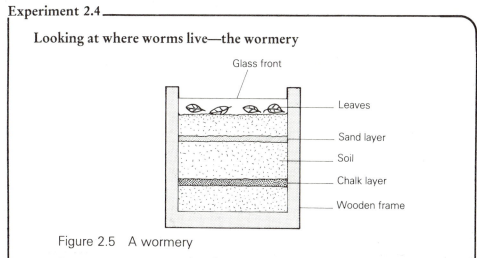

Figure 2.5   A wormery

1. Set up a wormery with a layer of sand and a layer of chalk sand-wiched between layers of soil (see Figure 2.5).

2. Put three or four worms on the top of the soil.

3. Add a few leaves for the worms to feed on.

4. Cover the whole wormery with several layers of newspaper to keep them in darkness as if they were under the ground.

5. Leave the wormery in a cool place for a few days.

6. After this time, remove the newspaper and see where the worms have gone. Make a sketch showing the worm burrows and any worm nests if you can see them.

2.4 The locust, a common lab insect

Insects, you will remember, all have six legs. The *locust* is a relative of the grasshopper and is quite easy to keep and is quite big. This is why it is often found in biology labs. It comes from North Africa where it is often found in huge numbers. These will occasionally form a *swarm* and fly over the countryside eating all the plants that they find. Such swarms are a great problem to the farmers in this area. Only adult locusts have wings. Young locusts are called *nymphs* or *hoppers* and there are five stages of nymphs called *instars*, each one is a little larger and more developed than the one before it. The fifth instar develops into the adult. These changes from one instar to the next, or from fifth instar to the adult, are called *moults*. The insect splits off its old exoskeleton and emerges. Then within a couple of hours its new exoskeleton will have hardened, but before it does, the insect blows it up to its full size by drawing in air. You may be able to see some cast off skeletons in your cage.

Experiment 2.5

Looking at locusts

1. Look at a locust and compare it with Figure 2.6. You may have to look at the locust in its cage or your teacher may provide you with one in a boiling tube or tied with a cotton 'lead' and attached to a stand.

2. Identify the head, thorax and abdomen. Look at the legs and the wings. Do all the legs have the same number of segments? Which part of the body are the legs and wings attached to? What are the third pair of legs used for?

3. Watch a locust walking. Is there a pattern to the way it moves its legs?

4. Try to describe how it walks.

5. Observe a locust feeding. What is it eating? Observe how its mouthparts work. Compare its mouthparts with Figure 2.7.

6. Describe how the locust feeds.

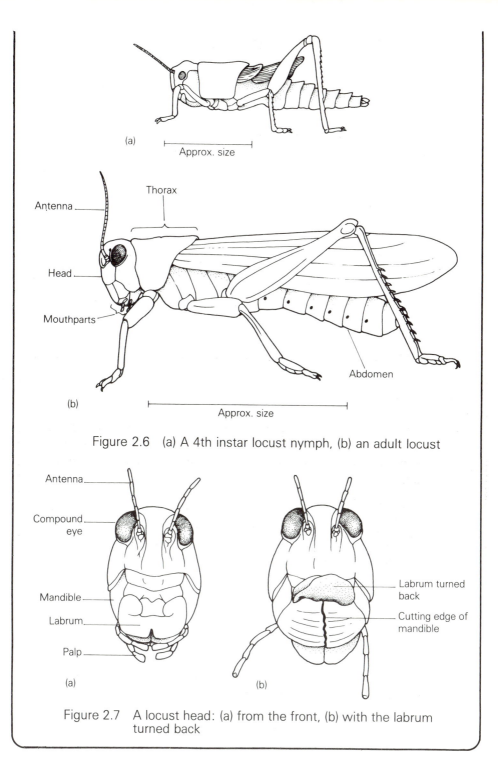

(a)

Approx. size

Antenna

Thorax

Head

Mouthparts

Abdomen

(b)

Approx. size

Figure 2.6   (a) A 4th instar locust nymph, (b) an adult locust

Antenna

Compound eye

Mandible

Labrum

Palp

(a)

Labrum turned back

Cutting edge of mandible

(b)

Figure 2.7   A locust head: (a) from the front, (b) with the labrum turned back

2.5 Man, another common organism

Looking at other animals is one way of finding out about what organisms do, but we can learn a lot by studying ourselves. We eat, sleep, move around and do many other things. You probably already know a great deal about how you do these. For instance, you know that your muscles make you move, and that by moving quickly for a while you can make your muscles tired so that you have to rest.

You may not know very much about what goes on inside you, and you are not very likely to get much chance to look inside another human. However, you can find out a lot by examining yourself from the outside. Let us look at some of the 'clues' we can examine to find out how we work.

The heart   You know that you have blood inside you and that it is *pumped* around your body by your heart. You can find how quickly your heart beats by finding your *pulse* and counting how many pulse-beats there are in a minute.

A pulse is where a blood vessel or tube, called an *artery*, comes over a bone near to the surface of the skin. If you squash the artery by pressing it with your forefinger you will feel the blood squeezing past. Each 'squeeze' or pulse-beat, is caused by the heart pumping the blood. There are many pulses in your body, but the easiest to find is the one in your wrist.

Experiment 2.6

Taking your pulse rate

1. Find the pulse in your wrist (see Figure 2.8).

2. Sit down quietly on your stool.

3. Count the number of pulses in a minute.

4. Now do some exercise, like running around the playground or up and down the stairs.

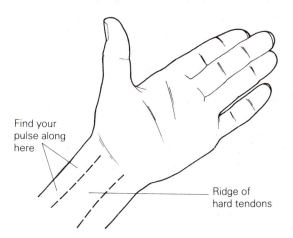

Find your
pulse along
here

Ridge of
hard tendons

Figure 2.8   How to take your pulse

5.   Count your pulses for a minute immediately after the exercise.

6.   Copy out the chart below and fill in your results.

Pulse rate before exercise	*Pulse rate after exercise*
_____ beats per minute	_____ beats per minute

7.   What caused the difference in your two results?

Breathing   You will have noticed that after running around you were panting and breathing more quickly than you usually do. This is linked to your speed-up in pulse rate because you breathe to get in enough oxygen to give your body, and in this case your muscles particularly, enough energy to work. Your blood carries the oxygen to the parts where it is needed and also removes the carbon dioxide which these parts produce. Therefore, the more oxygen you need, the faster you breathe and the quicker your heart pumps.

29

Investigating your breath

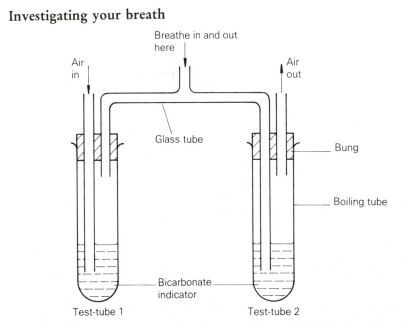

Figure 2.9   Apparatus for investigating human breath

1. Put about 2 cm depth of bicarbonate indicator into each clean boiling tube, making sure the indicator comes above the bottom of the long tube. Bicarbonate indicator turns yellow with carbon dioxide. Be careful not to handle the apparatus too much, since the perspiration on your fingers will interfere with the result.

2. *Gently* breathe in and out through the centre tube.

3. Watch for any changes and record them in a chart like the one below:

	Tube 1	*Tube 2*
Colour before breathing		
Colour after breathing		

4. Did you detect any carbon dioxide? Was it in the air you breathed in or the air you breathed out?

Do other organisms produce carbon dioxide?

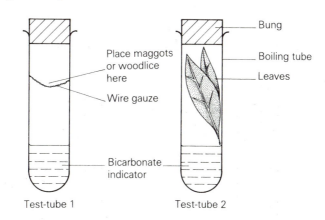

Figure 2.10 Apparatus for investigating 'non-human' breath

1. Put about 2 cm depth of bicarbonate indicator in two clean boiling tubes. Be careful not to breathe over the tubes or to handle the bungs too much since the perspiration on your fingers will interfere with the experiment.

2. Carefully place about six woodlice or maggots into test-tube 1.

3. Place a few leaves in test-tube 2.

4. Wait for about half an hour.

5. Gently swirl the bicarbonate indicator in the tubes, making sure you do not wet either the leaves or the animals.

6. Are there any colour changes?

7. Note any results and then return the animals to their container.

Lung volume

You now know more about what your lungs do, but how much air can they hold when they are full?

Finding the volume of your lungs

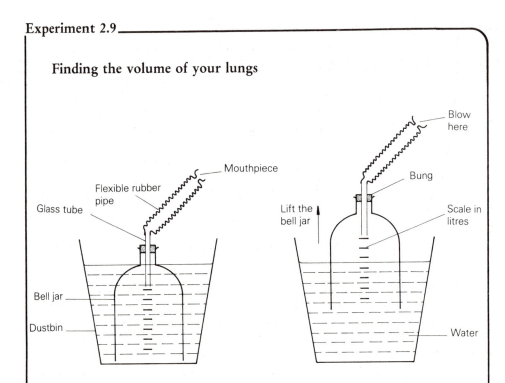

Figure 2.11 Apparatus for investigating lung volume

1. You must be careful when using this apparatus or you will make a lot of mess.

2. One person in the class must work the bell jar by lifting it as each person breathes in. He or she must also make sure that the water is level inside and outside the bell jar before the volume is read off the scale. Lower the jar slowly after each experiment or take the bung out to allow the air to escape easily.

3. Disinfect the mouthpiece before you use it.

4. Take two or three deep breaths, and then breathe in as deeply as you can. Gently breathe out into the mouthpiece as much air as you can from your lungs. At the end of your breath hold your position for a few seconds whilst the person working the bell jar has had time to read the scale.

5. Record all the class results in a table like the one below:

Lung volume	Number of people with that volume
½ litre	
1 litre	
1½ litre	
2 litre	
2½ litre	
3 litre	
3½ litre	
4 litre	

6. Write up the results in the form of a bar chart (see Figure 2.12).

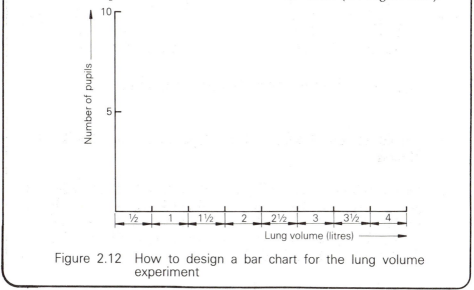

Figure 2.12 How to design a bar chart for the lung volume experiment

2.6 Plants in action

Looking at animals in action is quite easy, but plants do not seem to do very much. In the spring, trees which have been bare for months begin to grow more leaves. Plants everywhere grow and start to produce brightly coloured flowers. Both these actions are however quite slow, taking days or weeks to become complete.

33

It is possible to see that even when a plant does not seem to be doing a lot, it is performing actions which are essential if it is to stay alive.

Plants and water

All plants need water to live and without it they become limp and droop, a condition called *wilting*. If it is left for too long without water, then a plant will die, but usually a wilted plant will go back to its normal healthy state half an hour after being watered. You may have had plants at home which have done this. The next experiment investigates where the water travels in a plant.

Experiment 2.10

Investigating water movement in plants

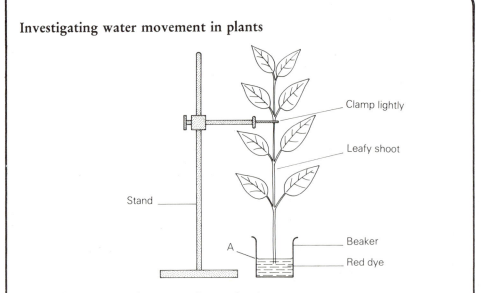

Figure 2.13   Apparatus for seeing how water moves in plants

1.   Get a leafy shoot such as that from a privet bush.

2.   Place it in a beaker containing some red dye or ink dissolved in water. Clamp the plant loosely so that it stands upright.

3.   Make a note of the time the experiment started.

4.   Wait for half an hour then remove the plant from the water. Mark the stem to show where the water in the beaker came to (point A on the diagram).

5. Starting near the top of the plant using a scalpel or scissors, cut the stem. Look into the cut end to see if you can see any red staining (you may need a hand lens). If you do not see any staining, then make a cut about 1 cm further down the stem. Continue to do this until you first see signs of red staining.

6. Measure the length of the stem from point A to the place where you first saw staining. How far had the stain travelled in half an hour?

7. Work out how far the stain would have moved in an hour and write this down in your results.

8. Make a cut further down the stem and use your hand lens to see exactly where the stain is in the stem. Is it spread evenly throughout the stem or is it in certain places only?

9. Make a clear sketch of the cut end of your stem (called a *cross-section*) showing and labelling exactly where the red stain has been carried up the stem.

10. Write down the class results for the distance the stain moved in a table like the one below:

Name of experimenter	Distance stain travelled
Average	

Work out the average distance for the class results.

Questions on Chapter 2

Write down the correct words to fill the gaps in these sentences:

1. The upper side of an earthworm is _____, whilst the lower side is _____.

2. The worm has _____ on its underside which it uses for _____.

3. Worm _____ are produced from the _____ which the worm eats.

4. Habitats may differ in their _____ and _____, and in the amounts of _____ and _____.

5. Young locusts are called _____, and there are _____ stages before the locust becomes an adult.

6. Locusts feed on _____, and in _____ where they originally come from they can be a great problem to the farmers.

7. The class results for a pulse rate experiment are as follows (all measured in beats per minute): 60, 75, 74, 66, 69, 72, 65, 70, 68, 71. Calculate the average pulse rate for the group. Do you think this group took their pulse whilst sitting still or after running around? Explain your answer.

8. The class results for a lung volume experiment are as follows (all measured in litres): 2, ½, 2, 1, 2, 1½, 2½, 1, 2½, 3½, 1½, 2, 2½, 3, 1, 2, 3, 2½, 2, 1½, 2, 2½, 1½, 2½, 1½. Collect the results into a proper results table and plot a bar chart of them.

9. Try the plant water movement experiment at home using two different sorts of plants. Does water move at the same rate in all plants?

10. Try the plant water movement experiment at home using two leafy shoots from the same sort of plant. Pick one shoot with lots of leaves and one with only a few (or take the leaves off the second shoot). Does the number of leaves affect how quickly the water moves?

Crossword on Chapter 2

Across

1, 7 down. Scientific name for the earthworm (9, 10)
5 North _____ is where the locust comes from (6)
6 Small pile of mud at the entrance to a worm's burrow (4)
8 Name given to a badger's home (3)

Down

1 Common lab insect (6)
2 Bristles on a worm (7)
3 Bees carry pollen in a pollen _____ on each of their legs (3)
4 Gas we produce and breathe out (6, 7)
7 See 1 across

Across (cont.)

9 Another name for a maggot (4)
11 An area in which an organism lives (7)
12 Where you would find your pulse (5)
13 _____ means 'half' (4)
15 A type of insect, often found flying at night (4)
17 The _____ end of a worm is flattened (4)
18 People with well-developed muscles are often called this (6)
19 An Amoeba may live in a _____ (4)
20 Colour of bicarbonate indicator after we have breathed into it (6)
21 Oxygen is used by the muscles to give them this (6)

Down (cont.)

9 Common relative of 1 down, found in this country (11)
10 Insects have this many legs (3)
12 Box for keeping worms in (7)
14 Where a worm lives underground (6)
16 Gas needed by animals (6)

Trace this grid on to a piece of paper, and then fill in the answers.

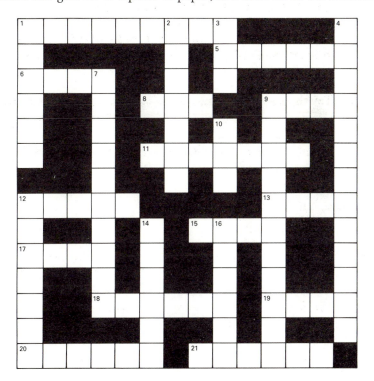

3. Building an organism

3.1 What are organisms made of?

When you looked in pond water you would have seen lots of very small organisms. The smallest of these, such as Amoeba and Euglena and Paramecium, are made of only one cell. The cell is the building block which organisms are made of, rather like the brick is the building block for houses. Some organisms are made of one cell and others of only a few. Most organisms, however, are made of a large number of cells joined together, and these are called *multicellular*.

Figure 3.1   Robert Hooke's microscope for observing cells

Robert Hooke (1635–1703) was the first scientist to describe cells. He used a microscope (rather like the one you use in school) to look at very thin slices of cork (see Figure 3.1). He found that the cork consisted of lots of little different-shaped boxes which he called *cells* and the name has been used ever since.

3.2 What cells are like

A multicellular animal, like a human, is made of millions and millions of cells. There are many different sorts, like blood cells, bone cells, brain cells, skin cells, and many more – see Figure 3.2 (a) and (b).

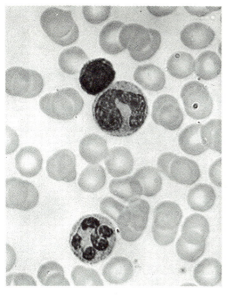

(a) Blood cells
     (overall magnification
      approx. × 1000)

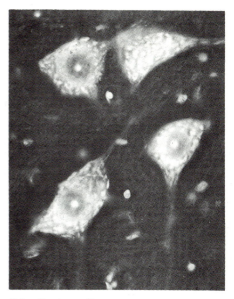

(b) Brain cells
     (overall magnification
     approx. × 450)

(c) Plant stem
     cells (overall
     magnification
     approx. × 130)

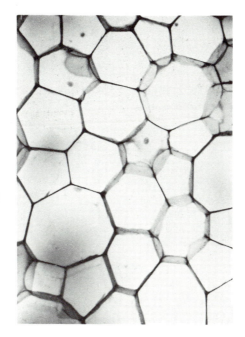

Figure 3.2   Different types of cell

Although these cells are very different in what they do and often in what they are like, they do have some features in common (see Figure 3.3).

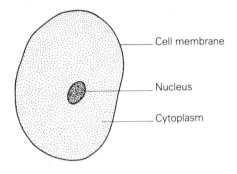

Figure 3.3   A typical animal cell

All cells have:

(a) A *membrane*. This is the thin outside layer which holds the cell together and keeps cells separate from each other. It also controls what sort of substances can pass in and out of the cell.

(b) A *nucleus*. This is a round object which can often be coloured with stains to make it more visible. It controls what the cell does and how it does it.

(c) *Cytoplasm*. This is a liquid which is three-quarters water and contains many tiny parts, much too small to be seen by a microscope. It is the living material of the cell and carries on all the activities necessary for life, like getting energy, making new substances and cells.

Just as plants and animals are different, so plant and animal cells are different too (see Figure 3.2). All animal cells have (a), (b) and (c) above.

Plant cells (see Figure 3.4) have these three also:

(d) A *cell wall*. This is a thick, fairly tough, layer around the membrane that helps plants to support themselves. For this reason many plant cells are angular or rectangular and plants are built up of these cells like a house is built of bricks.

(e) A large central *vacuole*. The vacuole is a large space inside the cell which contains a watery solution. Its purpose is to act as a store for some of the substances that the cell needs but mainly it helps to keep the cell rigid.

(f) *Chloroplasts*. These are green discs, scattered through the cytoplasm, which are able to trap sunlight and use the energy to make food.

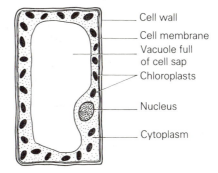

Figure 3.4   A typical plant cell

Experiment 3.1

Looking at plant cells

1. Get a clean microscope slide and place a drop of water in the centre of it.

2. Take a small piece of an onion.

3. Starting at a corner, using a pair of forceps, lift up the thin layer which covers the outside of the onion and peel off as much of this layer as you can (see Figure 3.5 over the page).

41

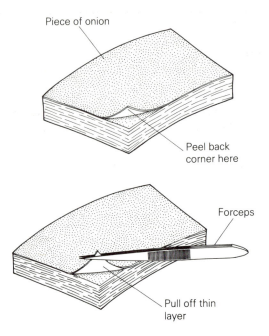
Piece of onion

Peel back corner here

Forceps

Pull off thin layer

Figure 3.5   Peeling a single layer of cells from an onion

4. Place the layer into the water on the slide so that it unrolls and lays flat (see Figure 3.6).

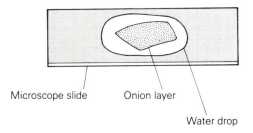
Microscope slide   Onion layer

Water drop

Figure 3.6   Preparing an onion layer for the microscope

5. Now examine the layer with the microscope. First go back and check the instructions for using the microscope on p. 16.

6. Draw large, clear diagrams of two or three cells. Label your drawing by using the diagram of the plant cell. Which parts can you see? Which parts can you not see?

Looking at animal cells

1. Take a clean microscope slide and a thin cover slip.

2. Using either a clean spatula or a clean finger nail (but wash your hands thoroughly first) gently scrape along the inside of your cheek.

3. Smear this scraping on to the centre of the slide.

4. Add one drop of methylene blue which will make the nuclei more visible.

5. Lower the cover slip on to the smear as shown in Figure 3.7.

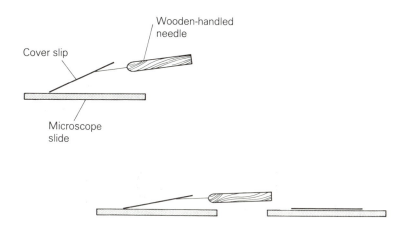

Figure 3.7   Lowering a cover slip

6. Examine the slide to find some cheek cells. These are very thin and hard to see. You will first see the tiny dark-blue nuclei, then as you look more carefully you will be able to see the cytoplasm and the cell membrane around it.

7. Draw large clear diagrams of two or three cells. Label your drawing by using the diagram of the animal cell.

3.3 Tissues

In multicellular organisms like man the cells are grouped together to form *tissues*. A tissue is a group of cells which all do the same job in the body. *Blood* is a tissue made up of blood cells, brain tissue is made of nerve cells. Plant stems are made of generalised plant cells called *parenchyma*.

3.4 Whole organisms—I. Plants

Not all plants are alike but they do all follow the basic plan of Figure 3.8. Their cells and tissues are organised into a number of parts which make up the whole plant.

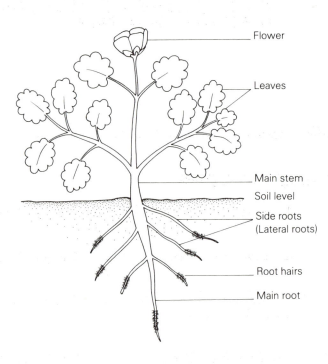

Figure 3.8   The parts of a plant

Roots   Roots are normally under the ground. They are generally white because their cells do not have chlorophyll. They anchor the plant in the ground so that it does not fall over or blow away in a wind. They also take in all the water that the plant needs.

44

Stem   The stem is the main stalk above the ground which holds all the leaves and flowers. Some plants have long stems, and some have very short ones. The stems of bushes and trees are thick and the stem cells are made much stronger by having lignin in their cell walls. The cells themselves die leaving a very hard substance called *wood*. The bench you are sitting at is probably made of it. The only living cells in a tree trunk are in a thin ring just under the bark.

Leaves   Green and flat and thin, leaves capture the sunlight using the chlorophyll in their cells. They make a plant's food using the Sun's energy, together with water and carbon dioxide gas in a reaction called *photosynthesis*.

Flowers   Flowers are the parts the plant uses for reproducing. They are often brightly coloured but not always.

Experiment 3.3 ─────────────────────

Looking at whole plants

1. Take a complete plant, and compare it with the diagram on p. 44.

2. Use a hand lens to examine it closely. Can you see root hairs?

3. Does your plant have one simple root with side branches or lots of roots all the same length?

4. Measure the length of the root and of the stem. Which is longer? Can you explain why?

5. Make a clear, labelled sketch of the plant.

6. Tidy up when you have finished.

Looking at root cells

1. Get a clean microscope slide and a cover slip.

2. Place a drop of water on to the middle of the slide.

3. Cut off the tip, 5 mm, of a cress root and put it into the water drop on the slide.

4. Put the cover slip on as in Experiment 3.2.

5. Cover with a small piece of blotting paper or paper towel and press gently on the cover slip to squash the root, as shown in Figure 3.9.

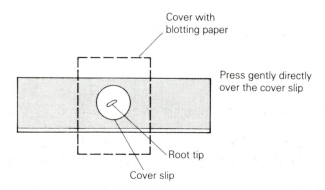

Figure 3.9   Preparing a root tip for the microscope

6. Look at your root to see root cells. You will only be able to see cells clearly where the root has been squashed to make it very thin.

7. Find as many different cells as you can and make a clear sketch of each of them.

3.5 Flowers

Many flowers are extremely pretty and smell very nice. We use them to decorate our homes and work places because they make them more cheerful. Although we find flowers very attractive, they are used in nature not to attract *us* but to attract insects so that the plant can reproduce. The insects carry pollen from one flower to another and the pollen from one flower will join with the ovule (or egg cell) of another similar flower to make a seed. This joining of pollen and ovule is called *fertilisation*.

As you have already discovered, there are lots of differences between most living organisms. There are differences between flowers too, but most flowers have the same parts as the buttercup drawn below although they may have different numbers of the parts (see Figure 3.10).

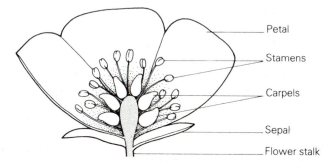

Figure 3.10   A buttercup cut in half

The parts of a flower are *sepals*, *petals*, *stamens* and the *carpel*.

Sepals

Sepals are small and green and look a little like leaves. They protect the flower before it opens, when it is still in the bud.

Petals

Petals are the parts which attract the insects. They are colourful and may have stripes or dots or patterns on them. Insects do not really see very well and the patterns make the flower stand out more. Petals may also have a *nectary* which produces a sugary liquid called nectar which the insects feed on. They may also produce *scent*. The parts of a petal are shown in Figure 3.11.

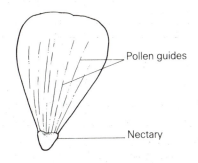

Figure 3.11   The parts of a petal

Stamens

Stamens produce the pollen in small sacs called *anthers* which are held on thin stalks called *filaments*. The pollen is inside the anther and is released when the anther splits open (see Figure 3.12).

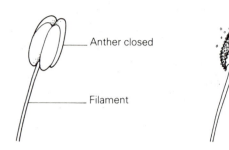

Figure 3.12   An anther

Carpel

The carpel has a number of parts, as shown in Figure 3.13. The *ovary* is the part which makes the *ovule* or plant egg. Some ovaries contain only one ovule whilst others contain many. The *stigma* is the platform which catches the pollen in its sticky surface. The *style* may be long or short but is only an extension to get the stigma into the best position for catching pollen.

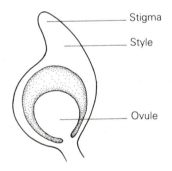

Figure 3.13   The parts of a carpel

3.6 Composite flowers

Plants like the daisy and the dandelion have flowers which are not like the buttercup. They are not a single flower but are made of hundreds of tiny flowers called *florets*. If you take a floret apart, you will see that apart from sepals, it has all the parts a buttercup has. Composite flowers get their name from the fact that they are composed of lots of florets.

Figure 3.14 shows a number of different sorts of flowers and gives you an idea of the sorts of arrangements you may find.

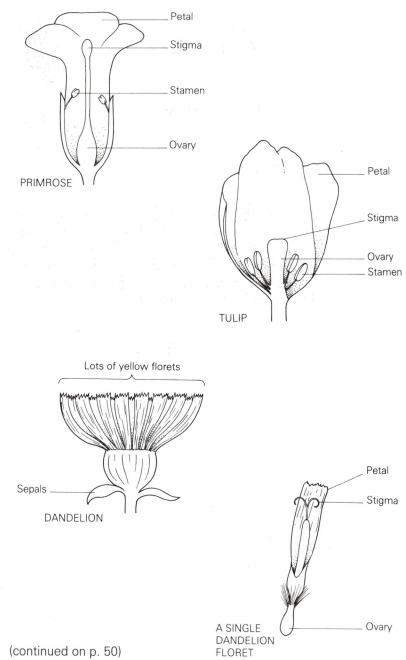

PRIMROSE

Petal

Stigma

Stamen

Ovary

TULIP

Petal

Stigma

Ovary

Stamen

Lots of yellow florets

Sepals

DANDELION

A SINGLE
DANDELION
FLORET

Petal

Stigma

Ovary

Figure 3.14 (continued on p. 50)

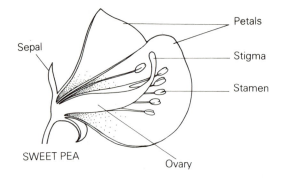

Sepal

Petals

Stigma

Stamen

SWEET PEA

Ovary

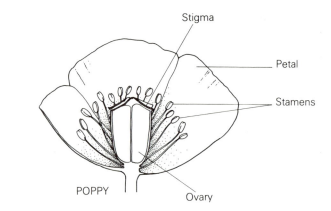

Stigma

Petal

Stamens

POPPY

Ovary

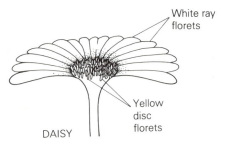

White ray
florets

Yellow
disc
florets

DAISY

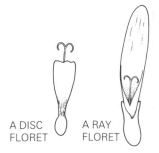

A DISC
FLORET

A RAY
FLORET

Figure 3.14   Some common flowers

Looking at flowers

1. Collect a flower and write down its name in your book.

2. Using forceps, carefully pull it apart and collect the sepals, petals, stamens and carpels. Count how many of each you have.

3. Get a strip of Sellotape and lay it upside down on the bench. Carefully stick on to it one each of sepal, petal, stamen and carpel. Now stick this strip down the left side of your book, as shown in Figure 3.15.

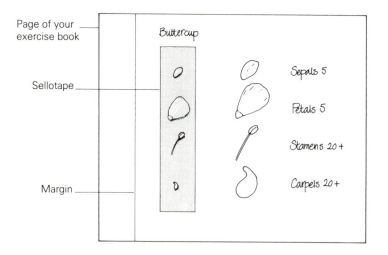

Figure 3.15   How to keep records of flowers

4. Down the centre of your page make a clear diagram of each of the parts.

5. On the right side of the page write down the name of the part and how many of them the plant had.

6. Do this for a number of different flowers.

3.7 Wind-pollinated flowers

Plants which need insects to carry the pollen from flower to flower are called *insect-pollinated*. Other plants just let the wind blow their pollen about, and these are called *wind-pollinated*. Because they do not have to attract insects they are not colourful and do not produce nectar or scent. These flowers are usually small and green, and we often do not notice them at all. All the grasses are pollinated by wind, and so are hazel, plantains, and the stinging nettle. Figure 3.16 shows what some of these flowers look like.

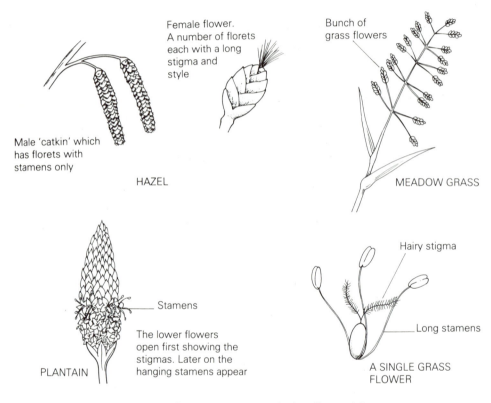

Figure 3.16   Some common wind-pollinated flowers

To make sure that pollen reaches other plants, wind-pollinated flowers are adapted in a number of ways. They have anthers which hang outside the flower and catch the wind easily. They also produce lots and lots of pollen to be blown around. It is this pollen which is responsible for the hay fever that many people suffer from. The stigmas too are long and hang outside the flower to catch the pollen.

Experiment 3.6

Looking at wind-pollinated flowers

1. Collect the flower of a wind-pollinated plant.

2. Using forceps and a hand lens, carefully pull the flower apart to find the parts. Count how many of each part there are.

3. Using Sellotape as in Experiment 3.5, stick the parts of the flower into your book.

4. Draw clear diagrams of the parts and write down their name and number as in Experiment 3.5.

3.8 Whole organisms—II. Man

Just as in plants, our cells and tissues are grouped together in a pattern which is the same or similar to many other animals. The biggest difference between Man and the other mammals is that we walk on two legs only and we have a much bigger brain. This allows us to learn and think more and therefore we can control more of what goes on around us. For the rest, the parts inside us are in the same place, doing the same job as inside many other animals.

Our bodies, like those of most animals, are like very complicated machines. They have many parts doing specialised jobs, and even if we could take a person apart we would still find it difficult to see how all the pieces work together.

Bones

Our bodies are built around an inner *skeleton* made of bones. In fact there are about 190 bones inside each one of us. Because it is inside, the skeleton is called an *endoskeleton*. Insects, you will remember, have their skeleton outside, and it is called an *exoskeleton*.

The bones of the skeleton are not fixed rigidly to each other but are held together by tough moveable wrappings called *ligaments*. Where two bones meet is called a *joint*, and this acts like a hinge. The muscles are arranged so that when they pull, the bones move whilst still being held together at the joint. We will study more of this in Chapter 10.

You may have a model skeleton where you can look at how the bones are arranged, but in the next exercise you will look more closely at the bones of the hand. Since there is not much muscle (often called flesh) in your hand, you can see or feel most of the bones.

Experiment 3.7

Looking at the bones of the hand

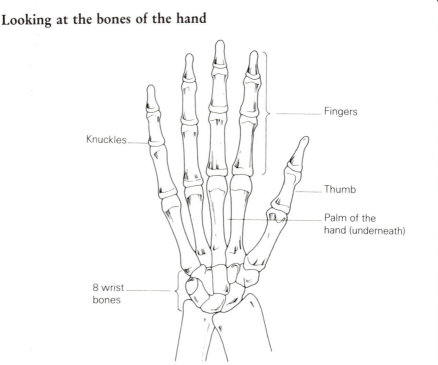

Figure 3.17   The bones of your left hand

1. Lay your left hand out on a large piece of paper. Spread your fingers widely apart.

2. Starting at your wrist, trace the outline of your hand and fingers with a pencil.

3. Mark faintly in pencil the position of the joints.

4. Using the diagram of the skeleton of the hand (Figure 3.17) draw the bones into your outline. The position of the joints should help you to draw the bones to their correct size.

5. Label your diagram.

Organs
        Many of the tissues in the body are grouped into structures quite separate from other parts. These are called *organs* and they each have a special job to do. Some examples of organs include the *heart*, the *lungs*, the *kidneys*, the *brain*, the *stomach* and the *intestines*.

In the following exercise you will be able to put the main organs into their correct positions in the body.

The organs of the body

1. Carefully trace the two halves of the outline of a person from Figure 3.18 on pp. 56–7.

   The halves have been drawn so that the upper part exactly fits the lower part at the dotted line. Using a large sheet of paper you can trace the upper half first and then match the lower half to it. In this way you will get a complete figure.

2. Trace out the organs from Figure 3.19 on pp. 58–9 on to another sheet of paper. You may colour them if you wish.

3. Cut out the organs and stick them on to the outline in the right place. Some organs are labelled 'Stick down this side only'. This is because they will cover up other organs. If you glue them properly, when the glue is dry you will be able to fold them back to see the organs underneath.

4. Label your model.

All the organs you have stuck in have particular jobs. Below is a list of what they do. You may already know some of them.

Brain
        The brain controls the body and makes sure it works correctly. It receives information about what is going on inside and outside the body and makes the body respond when necessary. In humans the brain is also able to think and to remember, to learn and to let us do things like read and write. In most other animals the brain cannot do this. Even the cleverest of animals can only learn and remember simple activities.

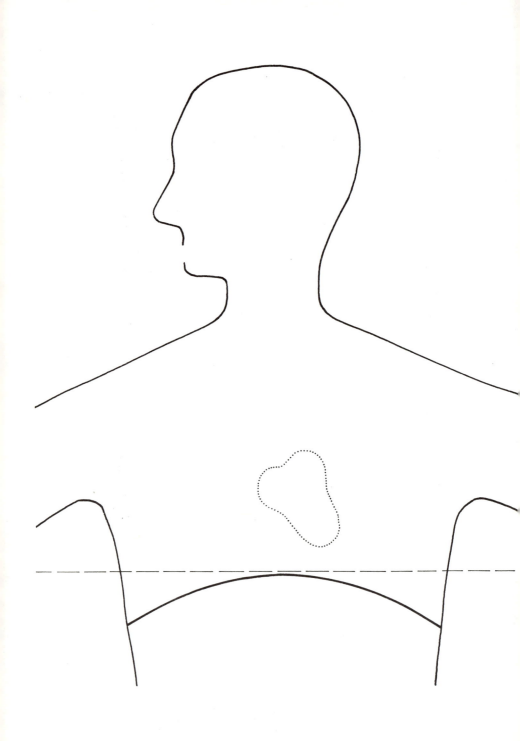

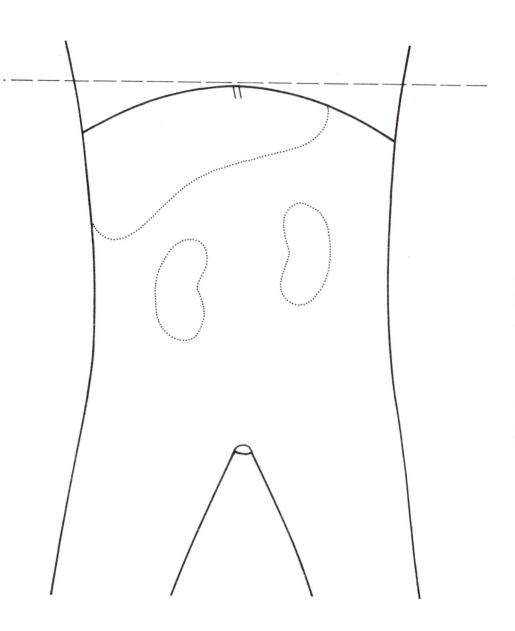

Figure 3.18   The outline of a human body

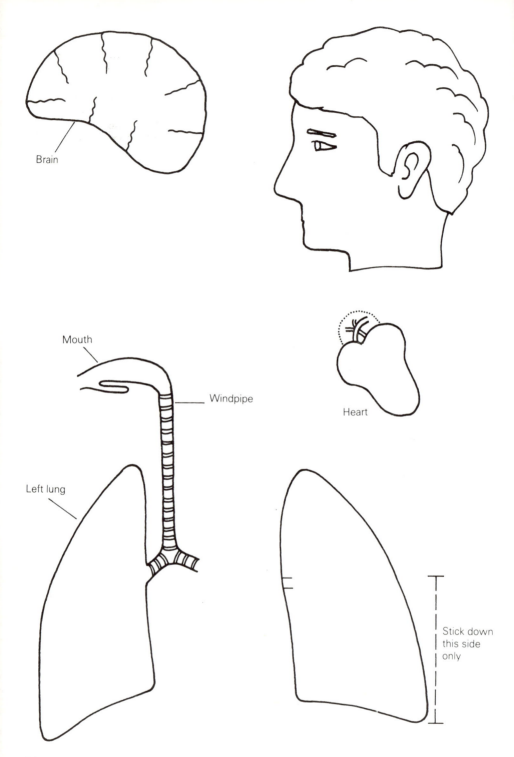

Brain

Mouth

Windpipe

Heart

Left lung

Stick down
this side
only

58

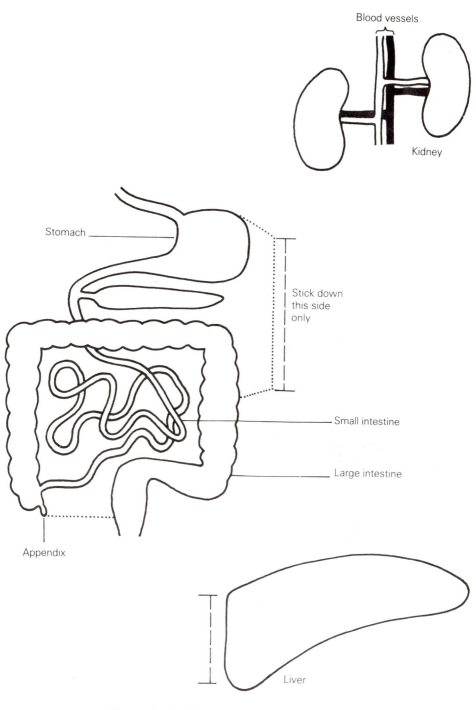

Figure 3.19   The organs of a human body

Lungs   Lungs take in air and take oxygen from it into the blood. They add carbon dioxide from the blood to the air and then push the air out again. This is called *breathing*.

Heart   The heart pumps the blood all around the body through a complicated system of tubes. The blood delivers oxygen and food and some other substances to all the parts of the body. There is usually enough food in the blood, but sometimes parts of the body may need more oxygen. Then the heart beats faster to deliver more.

Stomach and intestines

Your stomach and intestines are part of the digestive system which is an extremely long tube beginning at our mouth. Its job is first to change the food we eat into a form the body can use, a process called *digestion*. Then the digested food passes through the special walls of the intestines and into the blood to be carried around the body, a process called *absorption*. The *appendix* is a tiny finger-like tube attached to the side of the intestines. It has no job in humans, and occasionally becomes infected so that it has to be removed in a small operation.

Kidneys   Kidneys clean the blood and remove the poisonous substances that are made by the body as a normal part of the living process. They also get rid of water if we have too much. The liquid that the kidneys produce is called *urine* and is stored in the bladder until it is released at intervals during the day.

Liver   The liver is a complex chemical factory which makes many of the substances that the body needs from the foods that we eat. It also breaks down any unwanted substances.

Questions on Chapter 3

Write down the correct words to fill in the blanks.

1. _____, _____ and _____ are organisms made of only one cell.

2. Organisms made of lots of cells are called _____.

3. Cheek cells contain a _____, a _____ and some _____ only.

4. A group of cells which all have one job is a _____.

5. Plants can be pollinated by _____ or _____.

6. Make a list of the differences between plant and animal cells.

7. Man's skeleton is an _____ whilst that of an insect is an _____.

8. Where the bones of the skeleton meet is called a _____.

9. Make a leaf collection by finding the leaves of as many trees as you can. Place each leaf under a sheet of paper and gently rub over the paper with a soft pencil or wax crayon. This will produce an outline of the leaf showing its veins and shape. Arrange your leaves as neatly as you can on each sheet of paper. Label each leaf with the name of the tree it came from.

10. Make a flower collection by pressing some flowers between sheets of tissue and newspaper and placing them under a heavy book for a few days. Arrange the pressed flowers on sheets of plain paper and stick them down using small strips of Sellotape. Label the flowers neatly.

Crossword on Chapter 3

Across

4 A 'beating' organ (5)
5 They make a plant's food (6)
7 A composite is not just _____ flower (3)
8 A single-celled organism which has a whip-like structure at one end for movement (7)
9 Part of the digestive system (7)
16 Parts of a flower, often brightly coloured (6)
17 A common 10 down in Man (5)
18 Organ at the front of our face for breathing through (4)
19 Animal with six legs (6)
20 A whole organism (3)

Down

1 12 down is three-quarters _____ (5)
2 They produce pollen (7)
3 A limb for walking (3)
4 The first man to see cells (5)
5 What we breathe with (4)
6 Common one-celled animal (6)
10 Name for a group of cells (6)
11 It surrounds a cell (8)
12 Liquid in a cell (9)
13 Finger-like tube attached to the large intestine (8)
14 Pollen causes many people to suffer this (3, 5)
15 This cleans our 17 across (6)

Trace this grid on to a piece of paper, and then fill in the answers.

4. Organisms we cannot see

4.1 Microbes

The title to this chapter is not strictly correct, because we *can* see these organisms. They are extremely small and to see them clearly we have to use microscopes, sometimes very powerful ones. This is how these organisms got the name *microbes*. We can also see microbes when they are in groups of several thousand. A group like this is called a *colony*. Colonies are common and quite easy to see. An orange which has gone bad will often have patches of bluish green mould on it. This is a colony of *penicillium*, from which penicillin is obtained. Other moulds are colonies of different sorts of microbes.

There are three main sorts of microbes: *viruses, bacteria* and *fungi*.

Viruses   Viruses are extremely small, very simple living organisms which can only survive inside the cells of other living organisms. They cause a lot of diseases in animals and plants. Some diseases in man caused by viruses include smallpox, chicken pox, measles, German measles, colds and flu. Viruses are too small to be seen except by the most powerful microscopes.

Bacteria   Some bacteria are shown in Figure 4.1. They are single-celled organisms, but many are still extremely small. They occur everywhere in very large numbers. For instance, one gram of soil can contain as many as 2.5 billion bacteria. They are an extremely important group of organisms. The ones in the soil feed on dead plant and animal material making them rot or decay. Others in the soil feed on dead bacteria, changing some chemicals into others. In this way important substances get recycled and eventually become available for plants to use again. (See Figure 4.2 over the page.)

Tiny round bacteria which are held together in small groups are called *Staphylococci*. Bacteria like these cause blood poisoning

Rod-shaped bacteria like these are called *Bacilli*. Plain rods like the ones here can cause tuberculosis

Figure 4.1 (continued on p. 64)

Rods like these with spare sacs on one end are also called *Bacilli*. Ones like these cause tetanus

 Rods like these arranged in chains cause dysentery. They are also called *Bacilli*

 Spiral-shaped bacteria like these are called *Spirilla*. Ones like these can cause the venereal disease syphilis

Figure 4.1   Some different sorts of bacteria

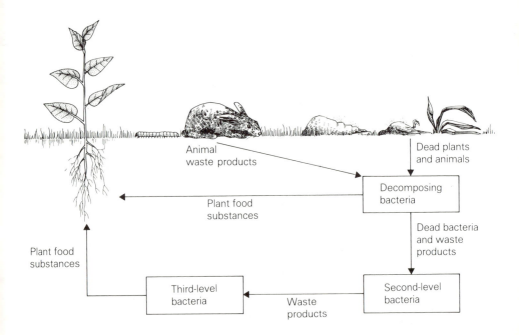

Figure 4.2   How bacteria in the soil recycles food chemicals

Some bacteria, like the viruses, live inside other organisms and cause disease. In Man these diseases include tuberculosis, pneumonia, whooping cough and some sorts of food poisoning.

Fungi   Some common fungi are shown in Figure 4.3. These are plants but are different to most plants because they do not have any chlorophyll. This means they cannot trap and use the Sun's energy to make food. They get their food from other living organisms, both dead and alive. Mushrooms and toadstools are common fungi, but because of their size they are not called microbes. The microbe we will look more closely at is a single-celled fungus called *yeast*.

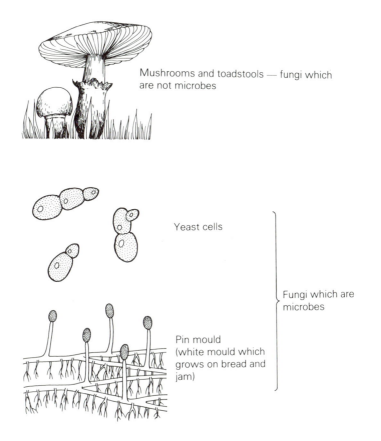

Mushrooms and toadstools — fungi which are not microbes

Yeast cells

Fungi which are microbes

Pin mould (white mould which grows on bread and jam)

Figure 4.3   Common fungi

4.2 Parasites and saprophytes

These two words describe how some living organisms feed. A *parasite* feeds by feeding off another living organism (called the *host*) whilst it is still alive. The host is usually harmed by the parasite. A *saprophyte* lives by feeding off the dead remains of organisms.

Many large animals too feed on other living organisms — for example, lions do. However, these are *not* called parasites, because parasites are *small* organisms. Larger animals, like lions, are given the name *carnivore*, *herbivore* or *omnivore*. Carnivores eat only meat and herbivores eat only plants, but omnivores eat both meat and plants, like most humans do.

Microbes are always either parasites or saprophytes.

4.3 The importance of microbes

Microbes are important because they exist everywhere. Even where you do not find microbes growing you will still be able to find tiny *spores*. These are produced in enormous numbers by all microbes and are carried by air and water. If they land on a surface which is good for growth, then the spore will *germinate* and produce a microbe. This can, if conditions are right, very quickly produce a new colony. Many microbes can reproduce themselves by each cell dividing into two new cells. Some bacteria can do this as quickly as once every half an hour. This means that a single bacterium, if it is in a good place to grow, can produce 16 777 216 new bacteria in only 12 hours.

Many microbes are harmful. They may cause disease in humans, or our animals and plants. They may also make our food go bad. Since microbes can reproduce so quickly, it would not take very long for an infection to grow once it had got started, and it could easily get out of control if we did not do anything about it. For this reason we must study the conditions in which microbes grow, to learn how to stop harmful microbes from affecting us too much.

Many microbes are very useful, as we shall see later. We need to encourage them to grow in order to get the best out of them.

4.4 Growing conditions for microbes

Like us, microbes need food and water to grow. They also grow quickest at the right temperature, but will still grow quite well even when conditions are cold. In fact microbes can survive and grow in places that humans could not, which is why they can be so dangerous.

Before you can do experiments on microbes you must learn the following words: *hygiene*, *disinfectant*, *sterilising*, *contaminate*, *pasteurisation* and *hypothesis*.

Hygiene   *Hygiene* means 'keeping clean'. Our bodies are very good places for growing microbes, and you must take great care not to let any get in. Always wash your hands after touching a container of microbes. Keep any cuts well covered with a plaster. Never open a container of microbes unless your teacher tells you it is safe to do so. Keep your bench clean and disinfected.

Disinfectant   *Disinfectant* is a chemical that kills microbes. It must be used on benches and wherever microbes are accidentally spilled.

Sterilising   *Sterilising* means 'killing microbes'. Things are usually sterilised by boiling them in water for at least 15 minutes. Your apparatus will be sterilised by heating in a large pressure cooker, called an *autoclave*, for 15 minutes. If you are using sterilised apparatus, touch it as little as possible since your fingers will have microbes on them which could spoil the experiment. There are microbes in the air too, so keep lids on.

Contaminate   To *contaminate* something means to let microbes or dirt get on it — when it should be kept clean. If you handle sterile containers with your fingers too much, you will contaminate them with microbes from your hands. In experiments with microbes you must be careful not to contaminate your experiment or to let any microbes you may have grown contaminate the lab.

Pasteurisation

Louis Pasteur was a French scientist who discovered, among other things, a way of killing most, but not all, the microbes in milk without having to boil it. Not everybody likes the taste of boiled milk so milk which has been *pasteurised* keeps its normal taste but, because it has fewer microbes, it can be kept for longer before it goes sour. The microbes in milk, by their feeding, will turn it sour and make it unfit for drinking.

Hypothesis   In Chapter 1 you read that scientists make careful guesses, or *hypotheses*, to answer the questions they have asked. Many of the experiments so far have been observing living organisms and it was not necessary to make a hypothesis. For some of the following experiments you will be either given a hypothesis or asked to make one up for yourself.

Investigating the conditions for microbes to grow

HYPOTHESIS: that microbes grow best when they have food, water and are warm

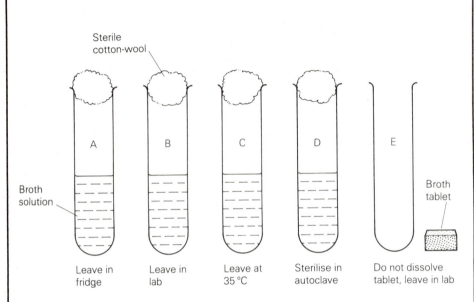

Figure 4.4   Apparatus for investigating microbe growth

1. Take five broth tablets, five sterile test-tubes, some boiled distilled water and some sterile cotton-wool. Label the test-tubes A, B, C, D, E.

2. Half fill the tubes A, B, C and D with boiled distilled water and dissolve one broth tablet in each. Keep the fifth tablet and tube E separate.

3. Leave all the tubes and the last tablet open to the air for 24 hours.

4. After this time treat them in the following way:

    Tube A.   Plug with sterile cotton-wool and place in the fridge.

    Tube B.   Plug with sterile cotton-wool and leave in the lab.

Tube C. Plug with sterile cotton-wool and leave in an incubator at 35 °C or in a warm place.

Tube D. Plug with sterile cotton-wool and then sterilise in the autoclave.

Tube E. Leave this and the spare tablet next to tube B in the lab.

5. After a few days, dissolve the last tablet in some sterile distilled water in tube E, then check the results. The microbes will have made the broth go cloudy, the more microbes then the more cloudy the broth. Record the appearance of the broth in a table like the one below:

Test-tube	Appearance
A	
B	
C	
D	
E	

6. Try to explain why the microbes grew well in some tubes but not in others. Was the hypothesis correct?

Experiment 4.2

Investigating the conditions for milk to go sour

1. Write down your own hypothesis for this experiment.

2. Take four sterilised test-tubes and remember to keep your fingers well away from the mouths of the tubes. Label them A, B, C and D and also with your group's initials so you will be able to recognise them.

3. Pour about 5 cm³ of fresh pasteurised milk into each tube and then plug them with sterile cotton-wool.

4. Treat the tubes in the following way:

Tube A. Place in the fridge.

Tube B. Place in the lab.

Tube C. Place in an incubator at 35 °C or in a warm place.

Tube D. Sterilise in an autoclave and then place in the lab.

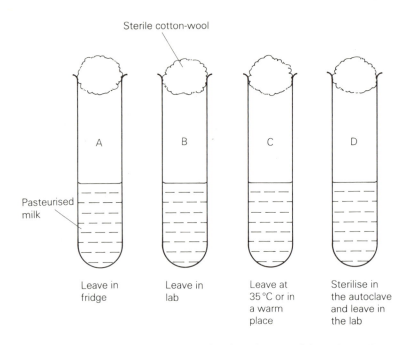

Sterile cotton-wool

A   B   C   D

Pasteurised milk

Leave in fridge

Leave in lab

Leave at 35°C or in a warm place

Sterilise in the autoclave and leave in the lab

Figure 4.5   Apparatus for investigating the conditions for milk to go sour

5. After two days check the tubes for signs that the milk has gone sour. Has it gone lumpy? Carefully remove the cotton-wool and smell the milk. Replace the cotton-wool quickly and be careful not to spill any milk. Leave the tubes where they were, and check again after another two days.

6. Record your results in a table like the one below:

Test-tube	Appearance of milk: fresh, sour, very sour	
	After two days	After four days
A		
B		
C		
D		

7. Was your hypothesis correct?

4.5 Pasteur's experiment

Figure 4.6   Louis Pasteur in his laboratory

Figure 4.6 shows Louis Pasteur (1822–1895) in his laboratory. Pasteur worked a great deal on microbes, small organisms which made things go bad. He was, at one time, very concerned with what made wine go off and become unfit for drinking. Scientists of Pasteur's time did not know much about microbes. They did not have good enough microscopes to see them clearly. All they usually saw was mould or cloudiness when food or drink had gone bad. Because they did not know any better they thought that food and drink, when it was left open to the air, went bad by itself and actually made the moulds. Pasteur himself did not believe this. He thought that microbes from the air entered the food and drink and made it go off. His problem, of course, was proving this since it was impossible to see the microbes and their spores in air.

In the end Pasteur did a simple experiment which showed that food and air could mix provided that the microbes and their spores were not allowed in.

The following experiment is exactly the same as the one Pasteur did, except that he did not use the same sort of flasks. Pasteur had to make all his own apparatus, or have it made for him, and so he used large round flasks with long necks. His most famous flask which he used for this experiment is called the swan-necked flask (you can see it on the bench in Figure 4.6).

Pasteur's experiment

HYPOTHESIS: that it is microbes in the air and not just air itself which makes broth go bad

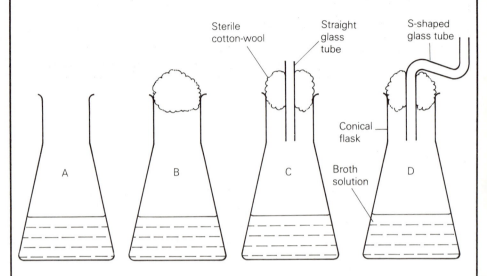

Figure 4.7 Apparatus for Pasteur's experiment

1. Take four 100 cm³ conical flasks labelled A, B, C, D.

2. Put four broth tablets and 40 cm³ of distilled water in each.

3. Treat each of the flasks as follows:

    Flask A. Do nothing.

    Flask B. Plug the flask with cotton-wool.

    Flask C. Plug the flask with cotton-wool with a piece of straight glass tube down the centre.

    Flask D. Plug the flask with cotton-wool with the S-shaped tube in it.

4. Sterilise all four flasks in the autoclave. Then remove and place in the lab. Leave them for one week.

5. After this time check the flasks for cloudiness.

6. Record your results in a table:

Flask	Appearance
A	
B	
C	
D	

7. Can you explain the result for flask D? Was the hypothesis correct?

4.6 Microbes around us

Not all microbes grow in liquids. Many need air to *respire* and so they grow on the surface of things. To see these we need to provide them with a surface to grow on. This is done by using a sort of jelly called *agar*, which can be heated to make it runny and left to set as it cools down. Because only a thin surface is needed to grow microbes the agar is used in a flat dish called a *Petri dish*. When the lid is on the Petri dish no microbes can get in even though the lid is not fixed down. (See Figure 4.8.)

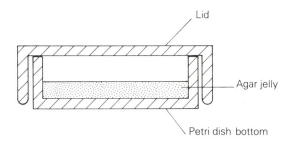

Figure 4.8   An agar plate

A dish like this with agar in it is called a *plate*. In the next experiment you will pour your own plate and then use it to grow some microbes.

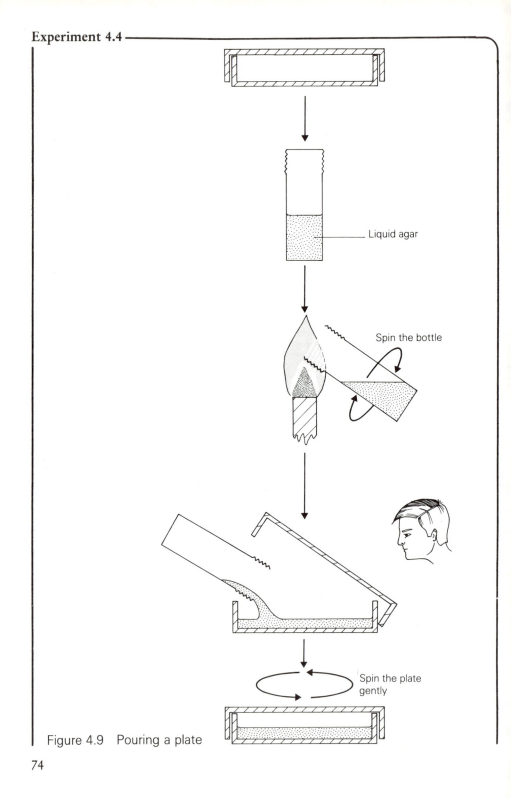

Liquid agar

Spin the bottle

Spin the plate
gently

Figure 4.9   Pouring a plate

Part I. Pouring the plate

Remember: everything you use will be sterile so try not to contaminate it.

The principle of this experiment is shown in Figure 4.9.

1. Work near a Bunsen burner. You will not need your own but can share with one or two other pupils. Be careful not to crowd each other.

2. Take a sterile Petri dish but do not lift the lid.

3. Take a bottle of agar, but *be careful*: it will be hot!

4. Remove the lid of the bottle and quickly spin the mouth through the Bunsen flame to kill any microbes. This is called *flaming*.

5. Lift the lid of the Petri dish from the side furthest away from you to stop your breath from going all over it. Quickly pour the agar in.

6. Put the lid back on the Petri dish and gently spin the dish to make sure the agar settles properly. Leave it to set.

Experiment 4.4 ————————————————————————

Part II. Growing microbes from around us

1. Work in groups of four with four plates. Label them A, B, C and D on the lid and also write your group initials.

2. *Plate A.* Sellotape the lid down on to the dish. This plate will check to see if there were any microbes in the agar or if any got in during pouring. It is called the *control*.

    Plate B. Leave this open to the air for half an hour. Then Sellotape the lid down.

    Plate C. Turn this plate over with the lid still on and draw a line across the bottom. Label one side 1 and the other 2 (as in Figure 4.10).

    Touch side 1 with an ordinary finger. Then very carefully wash your hands and touch side 2 with the same finger. Sellotape the lid down.

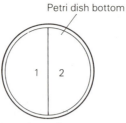

Petri dish bottom

1 | 2

Figure 4.10   Labelling plate C

Plate D.   Draw a line on the bottom of this and label the sides 3 and 4. Take some cotton-wool dipped in distilled water and wipe it across a surface in the lab. Then wipe it on to the agar. Do a different surface for 3 and 4. Sellotape the lid down. (See Figure 4.11.)

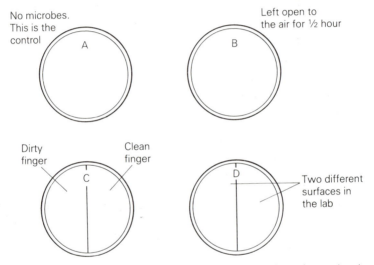

No microbes. This is the control   A

Left open to the air for ½ hour   B

Dirty finger   Clean finger   C

D   Two different surfaces in the lab

Figure 4.11   How to treat the four plates when investigating microbes

3.   Incubate the plates at 25 °C for a few days.

4.   Examine the plates and look for colonies of microbes growing on the surface. Do *not* take the lids off.

5.   Record your results by drawing the four plates, labelling the colonies of microbes.

6.   Which plate grew the most microbes? Did any grow on the control?

4.7 Controlling microbes

By now you will have realised that microbes are everywhere and that they can easily grow if conditions are right. If we are to live and eat as well as we would like, we must be able to control them.

Even as little as a hundred years ago a great many people died of diseases caused by microbes — diseases such as tuberculosis, typhoid, cholera, diphtheria, and many more. You will have heard of the plague or the Black Death. This was caused by bacteria carried by fleas, and during the 14th and 15th centuries many millions of people were killed as plagues swept across Europe.

Eating bad food was also very common, although it would seem strange to us now. People did not keep food in hygienic conditions, and much of it would go bad before it could be eaten. Even bad food could not be wasted, and so lots of salt and pepper and spices were used to hide the tastes.

After the time of Pasteur, scientists and doctors began to learn much about how to control microbes, and we must be very grateful to them for their work because without it our lives today would be very different.

Microbes can be controlled by either killing them, by preventing them from getting into places where they can cause harm, or by preventing them from growing even if they get there. These methods are used to keep food in a state where we can still eat and enjoy it. This is called *food preservation*, and there are a number of ways of doing it. You should remember that all these ways may alter the taste of the food and not all the ways are suitable for all foods. Many people still insist that fresh foods taste best.

Bottling and canning

Figure 4.12   Sealed food

Some food is kept in sealed tins or bottles (see Figure 4.12). Sometimes food will be sterilised before it is put into the container or it may be put in with a liquid which prevents microbes from growing. The syrup in tinned fruits does this.

Drying

Figure 4.13   Dried food

Microbes cannot grow without water and so dried foods (as in Figure 4.13) cannot go bad.

Cooling and freezing

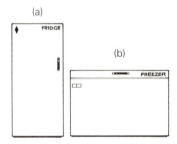

Figure 4.14   Cooled and frozen food containers

Microbes are not killed by cold, but they grow very slowly or not at all. Since refrigerators (Figure 4.14(a)) became common in houses people have been able to keep many foods such as meat, milk, eggs, butter, etc. for much longer than they used to. Even so, food may still spoil in the fridge. Freezing stops all microbe growth and food can be kept frozen for a long time (Figure 4.14(b)). After several months, however, food dries out in a freezer and is not so nice to eat afterwards. You should remember that frozen foods still contain microbes which will grow and reproduce once the food has thawed out. If this food is refrozen, then these microbes are frozen with the food waiting to grow as soon as the food is thawed again. In this way the number of microbes in the food may increase until there are sufficient of them to cause food poisoning when the food is eaten. For this reason food should never be frozen twice.

Pasteurisation

Figure 4.15   Milk and cream are pasteurised

This process is used only for milk and cream (Figure 4.15). These are heated to 71.7 °C for 15 seconds and then rapidly cooled. This kills the harmful microbes which make milk go sour.

4.8 Microbes and disease

Table 4.1 Some diseases caused by microbes	
Microbe	*Name of disease*
Viruses	Measles Mumps Small pox Chicken pox Polio
Bacteria	Tuberculosis Tetanus Pneumonia Blood poisoning Whooping cough Typhoid
Fungi	Ringworm Athlete's foot

Controlling diseases is often a case of controlling microbes (see Table 4.1). Figure 4.16 over the page, shows Joseph Lister (1822–1912), one of the first doctors to realise this. He worked in a hospital in Glasgow and became worried because many of his patients died after operations. They did not die because of his surgery but because their wounds became septic and full of pus. They then died of blood poisoning. The chances of blood poisoning were high because not only were the wards and beds quite dirty, but doctors used instruments which were never sterilised. They also wore their old coats during operations to stop

Figure 4.16   Joseph Lister

blood from getting on their clothes. Lister used carbolic acid to sterilise the instruments, his hands, the patients' wounds and even the air by using a special spray (see Figure 4.17). In this way he was able to make huge improvements in the survival rate of his patients.

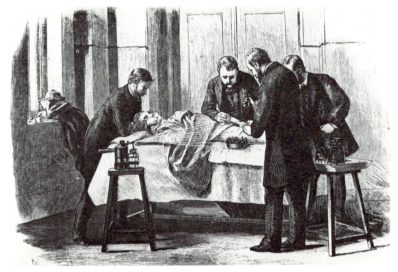

Figure 4.17   Joseph Lister's carbolic spray

Today hospitals are very clean, hygienic places. Microbes are killed by the regular use of disinfectants. Clean conditions are now found in our homes too. Places where microbes could breed, such as sinks and toilets, are kept clean by disinfectants. The next experiment investigates how well they work.

Investigating disinfectants

HYPOTHESIS: that disinfectants always kill microbes

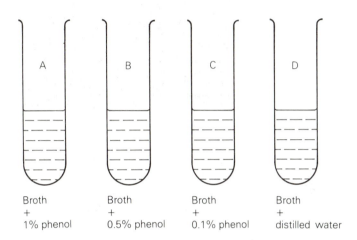

Figure 4.18 Apparatus for investigating disinfectants

1. Take four test-tubes and label them A, B, C, D.

2. Using a measuring cylinder add 5 cm³ of broth to each tube.

3. Treat each tube as follows:

    Tube A.   Add 5 cm³ of 1% phenol or some other disinfectant. This
    is about the same strength of disinfectant as you use at home.

    Tube B.   Add 5 cm³ of 0.5% phenol.

    Tube C.   Add 5 cm³ of 0.1% phenol.

    Tube D.   Add 5 cm³ of distilled water. This tube has no disinfectant
    and is the control. Remember to rinse out your measuring cylinder
    with distilled water each time you change to a new strength of
    disinfectant.

4. Leave your tubes in a test-tube rack in the lab for a week. Where
    microbes have grown the broth will become cloudy.

5. After a week check to see if microbes have grown. Write your results in a table:

Test-tube	Appearance of broth	Microbes grown
A		
B		
C		
D		

6. Was the hypothesis correct?

4.9 Useful microbes

Apart from the useful microbes which live in soil and help to recycle important chemicals, there are some microbes which are so useful that we grow and use them in large quantities. One of the most common useful microbes is *yeast*. There are a number of different yeasts but they all feed on sugar turning it into *carbon dioxide* gas and *alcohol* (the proper name is *ethanol*).

Bread making uses yeast mixed with a little sugar in the dough. The carbon dioxide gas forms little bubbles inside the dough but cannot escape, and so as more and more gas is produced the dough swells up. This is called letting the dough *rise*. This process usually takes half an hour to an hour, and the dough is left in a warm place. You should be able to explain why a warm place is important.

Once the dough has risen it is baked in an oven until the outside is brown and the inside is well cooked. Any alcohol produced by the yeast evaporates out of the bread during the baking.

Experiment 4.6

Making bread

1. Wash your hands and wrists thoroughly. During this experiment do not let the dough touch the bench (can you explain why?).

2. Working in pairs, each pair will need 150 g of plain flour, 1 g of salt, 5 g of sugar, 2 g of dried yeast and 100 cm^3 of warm water in a clean container. Each group also needs a mixing bowl and a spare clean beaker or cup.

3. Put about 1 cm depth of water into the spare beaker and add the yeast and the sugar (Figure 4.19). Gently swirl the beaker to mix the ingredients.

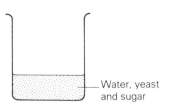
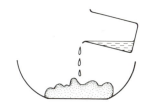

Figure 4.19   Starting to make bread   Figure 4.20   Add water slowly and mix

4. Put the flour into the mixing bowl with the salt. Add about 20 cm^3 of water and carefully mix this in with your hands.

5. Add the yeast/sugar water and mix it thoroughly in.

6. Continue to add slowly the water and mix until you have a solid lump of dough (Figure 4.20). Do not add too much water or the dough will become a sticky mess. You will have to add more flour if this happens.

7. Knead the dough (Figure 4.21). This means stretch the dough and fold it into the middle. This helps to mix in the yeast and makes the dough stiff. You must knead for at least 5 minutes or more to make a good mixture.

Figure 4.21   Knead the dough

8. Divide the dough into half so that each person has some. Shape it into a bun and put it on to a baking tray (Figure 4.22). You may like to make your bun a particular shape or to write your initials in the top of it.

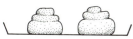

Figure 4.22   Two buns ready to rise

9. Your teacher will arrange for the buns to be kept in a warm place to rise and then for them to be baked.

10. Wash your hands and tidy up your bench.

11. When you get your bun back, before you eat it, answer these questions. Did it rise properly? Can you find the holes inside made by the carbon dioxide gas?

Beer and wine

In beer and wine making, yeast is used to produce alcohol as well as gas. This process is called *fermentation*. In some wines the gas is allowed to escape but in wines like champagne and in beers some of the gas is trapped to make the drink fizzy. Alcoholic drinks are pleasant to drink and the alcohol in them can make us more relaxed. Alcohol, however, is poisonous, and if too much is drunk it will kill. Long before this stage is reached, alchohol makes you drunk. It slows down your reactions and makes you sleepy, and it can make you sick. It can also make you violent, and drinking too much is responsible for a lot of fights between people. Even small amounts of alcohol make you unfit to drive because your reactions are too slow and you tend to drive too fast. For this reason you are not allowed to drive with more than 80 mg of alcohol to every 100 cm^3 of blood.

Some people say that drinking does not affect them but they are wrong. Drinking affects everybody, but more especially young people which is why you are not allowed to buy alcoholic drinks until you are 18.

Drinking alcoholic drinks with friends can be very enjoyable and will cause no harm if it is controlled. Drinking too much almost always causes harm of some sort, either to your body or to others around you. Regular drinking leads some people to becoming alcoholics. They are people who cannot live without an alcoholic drink of some sort. We must all control our drinking and not let it control us.

In the next experiment you will ferment some fruit juices to make a sort of wine. You are not allowed to drink this because the conditions for fermentation are not perfectly sterile — and you are of course too young anyway!

Investigating fermentation by yeast

1. Read the instructions and write your own hypothesis for this experiment.

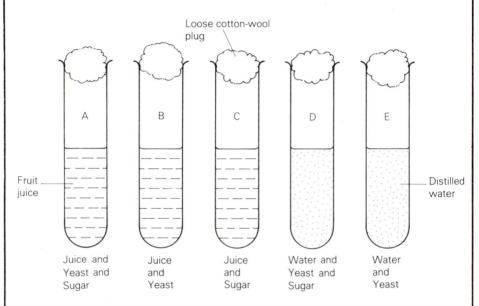

Figure 4.23   Apparatus for investigating fermentation by yeast

2. Take five test-tubes and label them A, B, C, D, E.

3. You will also need some fruit juice, some dried yeast, some sugar, distilled water and a clean spatula.

4. Treat the test-tubes as follows:

Tube A.   Add 10 cm³ of fruit juice + 3 granules of yeast and 1 spatula of sugar.

Tube B.   Add 10 cm³ of fruit juice + 3 granules of yeast.

Tube C.   Add 10 cm³ of fruit juice + 1 spatula of sugar.

Tube D.   Add 10 cm³ of distilled water + 3 granules of yeast and 1 spatula of sugar.

Tube E.   Add 10 cm³ of distilled water + 3 granules of yeast. (See Figure 4.23.)

5. Plug each tube lightly with cotton-wool, and then leave the tubes in a test-tube rack in a warm place.

6. After a week carefully examine each tube for signs of fermentation. You may see bubbles of gas or changes in the appearance of the liquid. There may be more yeast showing that it has reproduced, and you may notice a change in the smell. Record your results in a table:

Test-tube	Changes in appearance	Fermentation
A		
B		
C		
D		
E		

7. Was your hypothesis correct?

Cheese and yoghurt

Both cheese and yoghurt are made by mixing bacteria with milk. Different sorts of bacteria make the different sorts of cheese we can buy. The bacteria turn the milk into a solid part called *curds*, which floats on a liquid part called *whey*. The curds are skimmed off and more bacteria are added to turn them into cheese. Yoghurt is made by fermenting milk using different bacteria.

Vinegar   Yeast ferments the sugars in potatoes or apples or grain and produces alcohol. Vinegar bacteria then turn the alcohol into vinegar.

Sewage   Sewage waste from our toilets and sinks is made harmless by millions of microbes in the sewage works. After sewage has been treated by microbes it is clean enough to be put into the rivers again.

Penicillin   Penicillin is an antibiotic, a chemical used to kill microbes which cause disease in people. It is obtained from the blue Penicillium moulds.

Questions on Chapter 4

Write down the missing words from the following sentences.

1. The smallest microbes are called _____. They can only live inside the cells of other organisms. _____ are larger and are single-celled. Fungi are _____ which do not have chlorophyll. They are not all microbes. For example, _____ and _____ are not, but _____ is a microbe.

2. Microbes are important because many of them can cause _____. To grow well microbes need _____, _____ and _____, and they can get all three of these inside the human body.

3. If we do not use good _____ such as washing hands before a meal, we may _____ our food with microbes and make ourselves ill.

4. _____ is a jelly which is used in _____ dishes to grow microbes. Microbes grow on its surface because they need air for _____.

5. Write down as simply as you can, exactly what Pasteur proved with his famous experiment.

6. List the precautions you must take when pouring a plate.

7. Make a list of five foods which are preserved by each of the following methods: bottling, canning, drying, freezing.

8. Why did Joseph Lister try to control microbes in his hospital, and how did he do it?

9. What substances are produced by fermentation by yeast?

10. Write down the main reasons why drinking too much alcoholic drink is bad for you.

Crossword on Chapter 4

Across

4 On a plate, this must be taped down (3)

6 Means 'to let 3 down or dirt in' (11)

8 Man who first introduced sterilisation to hospitals (6)

9 A type of 15 down (7)

11 Very small, single-celled organisms (8)

12 The 11 across in milk make it go _____ (4)

16 A common illness in children, when they come out in spots, is _____ pox (7)

17 Dish for growing 3 down in (5)

18 Liquid made by fermentation (4)

19 There are enormous numbers of spores in the _____ (3)

20 A common useful fungus (5)

21 Means 'keeping clean' (7)

Down

1 Penicillin is one (10)

2 French scientist (7)

3 Very small living organism (7)

5 11 across in the soil feed on _____ plant and animal material (4)

7 Apparatus for sterilising equipment (9)

10 A 15 down of the lungs, caused by a 11 across (9)

13 This is made by fermenting milk using different 11 across (7)

14 A _____ wound is often full of pus (6)

15 Some 11 across live inside other organisms and cause _____ (7)

16 Broth which is _____ shows the presence of 3 down (6)

Trace this grid on to a piece of paper, and then fill in the answers.

5. Growing new plants

5.1 Where do new plants come from?

Figure 5.1   Growing from seed

If you want to grow some flowers or vegetables in your garden, you buy a packet of seeds and sow them. Then, if the conditions are right, the seeds grow into the plants you want (see Figure 5.1). Nature, of course, does not use seeds from packets. Originally the seeds came from parent plants which would release them to be blown by the wind, or carried by animals, or just dropped to the ground. This is called *seed dispersal*. Some people collect the seeds before they are dispersed and put them in packets to sell. In this way we can all get the seeds of many different plants very easily.

Sexual reproduction

Each seed is produced by a plant egg, called an *ovule*, being fertilised by a *pollen grain*. We call the ovule and the ovary which produces it and the other parts of the carpel that you saw in Chapter 3 the *female* parts of the flower (see Figure 5.2). The pollen and the anther which produces it and the other parts of the stamen are called the *male* parts of the flower (see Figure 5.3).

Fertilisation is where the male cell joins with the female cell. Together they produce a single cell which can grow into a new organism. The single cell produced in this way is called the *zygote*.

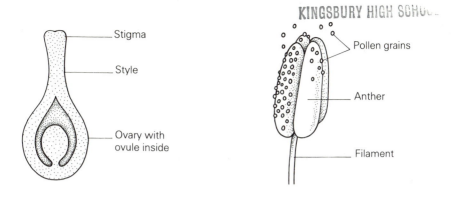

Figure 5.2   The female part of a flower   Figure 5.3   The male part of a flower

It will grow and divide to make many cells called the *embryo*. This sort of reproduction, which needs male and female cells, is called *sexual reproduction* and most plants and animals reproduce like this. (See Figure 5.4.)

There is a sort of reproduction which does not need male and female cells. This is called *asexual* reproduction and we will look at this later in the chapter.

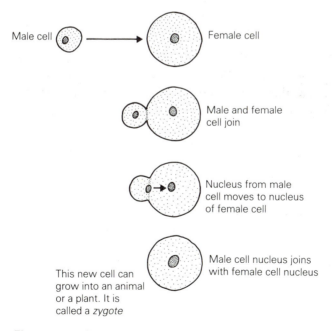

Figure 5.4   Sexual reproduction

5.2 Pollination

Unlike humans who exist as separate males and females, many plants have flowers which have both stamens and carpels. This means that the pollen from the anther could fertilise the ovule of the same flower. This is called *self-pollination*. Even though this is simple and easy, it is better for ovules to be fertilised by pollen from another plant. This is called *cross-pollination*, and it produces seeds which grow into stronger, healthier plants. Self-pollination may produce weak plants which do not grow so well.

Many plants have adapted so that only cross-pollination can take place. Some have separate male and female flowers where some flowers do not grow any carpels and others do not grow any stamens. In some flowers which have both stamens and carpels, they grow and ripen at different speeds so that the anthers ripen and release their pollen before or after the carpel is ready to receive it.

Pollen

Pollen is made inside the four pollen sacs of the anther. These sacs split open when the anther is ripe and release the pollen (see Figure 5.5).

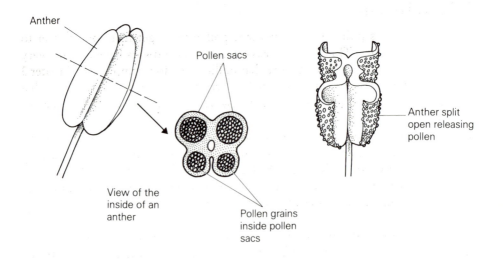

Figure 5.5 The release of pollen

Experiment 5.1

Looking at anthers and pollen

1. Remove a ripe and an unripe anther from a flower using forceps.

2. Look at both using a hand lens.

3. Make simple sketches of each. Can you see where the ripe anther has split?

4. Take a microscope and a clean glass slide. Set up the microscope as indicated on p. 16.

5. Dust some of the pollen from the ripe anther on to the slide and examine under low power.

6. Make a simple sketch of two or three pollen grains.

7. Repeat this using anthers from different plants.

8. Do all pollen grains look the same?

5.3 Fertilisation

Cross-pollination means that pollen must get from one flower to another. This is not an easy process and flowers have become very specialised to make sure that pollination does happen. In Chapter 3 you saw that pollen can be carried by wind or insects and that plants are adapted to be either wind-pollinated or insect-pollinated.

Once pollen has reached the stigma of the carpel it then has to get to the ovule. To do this the pollen grain splits open and a tube grows out. The tube then grows into the stigma and through the style to the ovule. You can see this process over the page in Figure 5.6, which shows a buttercup carpel.

The pollen grain splits originally because of the sticky, sugary liquid which the stigma produces. This feeds the pollen and allows it to grow the tube. You can grow pollen tubes too by soaking pollen in a sugar solution.

93

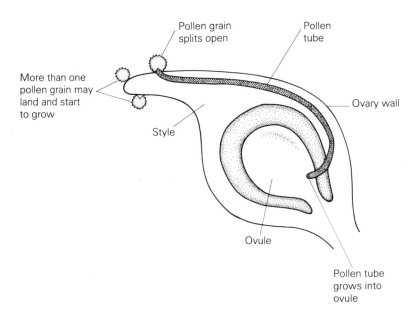

Figure 5.6   A buttercup carpel

Table 5.1 The differences between insect-pollinated and wind-pollinated flowers	
Insect-pollinated flowers	*Wind-pollinated flowers*
(1) Have large brightly coloured flowers	(1) Flowers are small and green
(2) Often produce nectar	(2) Anthers hang out of the flowers and produce enormous amounts of very light pollen
(3) Pollen is sticky or spiky so that it easily attaches to insect	(3) Stigmas are usually large and feathery and hang outside flower to catch pollen
(4) Flowers are often special shapes to allow only certain insects in	

Growing pollen grains

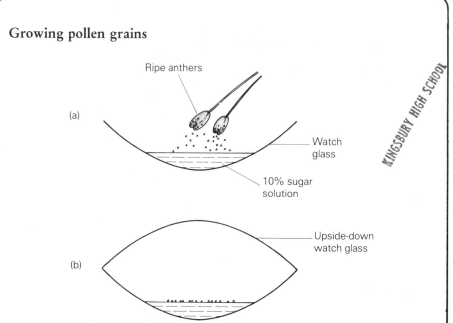

Figure 5.7   Growing pollen grains

1. Take a watch glass and add 5 or 6 drops of 10% sugar solution using a pipette.

2. Dust some pollen from a ripe anther on to the sugar solution (see Figure 5.7(a)).

3. Cover with an upside-down watch glass and leave for between one and two hours (see Figure 5.7(b)).

4. Set up a microscope as you have learnt to do.

5. Remove the top watch glass and put the lower one with the pollen grains on the microscope stage. Be careful not to spill the sugar solution.

6. Examine the pollen to see if any tubes have grown.

7. Make a labelled sketch of a pollen tube.

When the pollen tube reaches the ovule, the nucleus from the pollen tube cell fertilises the nucleus from the ovule to produce the zygote.

5.4 The seed

After fertilisation the seed or seeds start to grow. The flower petals and stamens will drop away, leaving only the ovary or ovaries which swell as the seed grows. The seed itself is growing in two parts. There is the part which will become the new plant which is the *embryo*. It consists of a *plumule*, which will grow into the shoot of the plant, and the *radicle* which will become the root. The other part of the plant is the *food store* for the embryo. When the embryo germinates and starts to grow, it will be some time before it is able to make its own food. It must therefore have a good supply of food to start its life. This food is as good for animals as it is for plants and many animals eat plant seeds because of their stored food. We eat many foods made from wheat seeds, such as bread, or barley seeds, or maize (corn on the cob), or rice which we usually eat in the form of the complete seed.

Not all seeds are exactly the same but they all have an embryo and a food store (see Figure 5.8).

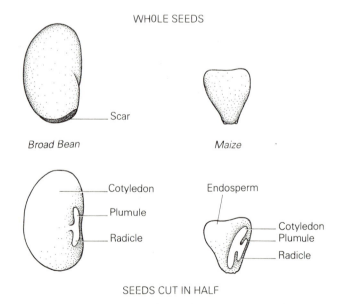

WHOLE SEEDS

Scar

Broad Bean

Maize

Cotyledon

Plumule

Radicle

Endosperm

Cotyledon
Plumule

Radicle

SEEDS CUT IN HALF

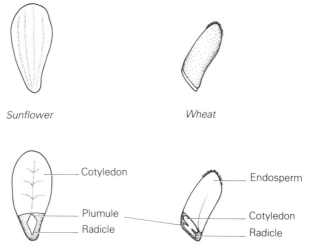

Figure 5.8   Different sorts of seeds

Experiment 5.3

Looking at plant seeds

1. Take a soaked seed of a bean or pea, a sunflower and maize or wheat.

2. Dry the outside so that you do not get water everywhere.

3. Compare the seeds with the diagrams in Figure 5.8. Make a sketch of each seed.

4. Put one seed on a board or glass plate and carefully cut it in half with a scalpel as in Figure 5.9. Remember: scalpels are sharp.

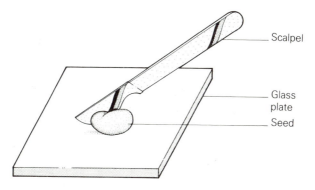

Figure 5.9   Cutting a seed

5. Compare your seed with the diagram and find the cotyledon, plumule and radicle.

6. Make a labelled sketch of the seed.

7. Do the same for your other seeds.

5.5 Seed dispersal

Seeds must be scattered as far as possible from the parent plant so that they do not crowd each other out when they germinate. As you can imagine, there are many different ways which plants use to disperse their seeds but these ways fall into three main groups: (a) wind-dispersed, (b) animal-dispersed, (c) self-dispersed. A few plants like the coconut use water to float their seeds away.

The way that a seed is dispersed is linked to what happens to the ovary after fertilisation. Once again there are many, many differences between plants, and you will not find all of them in this book. You will find a few examples so that when you look at plants on your own you may be able to understand how it works even if you have never studied it.

The fruit Although we use the word *fruit* for apples and oranges, in the strict scientific sense the fruit is the ovary and ovule of the plant. The ovary wall grows and develops as the seed grows and may become shaped in a particular way depending on how the seed is to be dispersed.

Wind-dispersed seeds

Here the seeds may be light as in the poppy, and are simply blown around. In others the whole fruit is dispersed and the ovary wall has grown a wing as in the sycamore. The dandelion has a parachute of hairs attached to the ovary wall which helps it to be carried by the wind. (See Figure 5.10.)

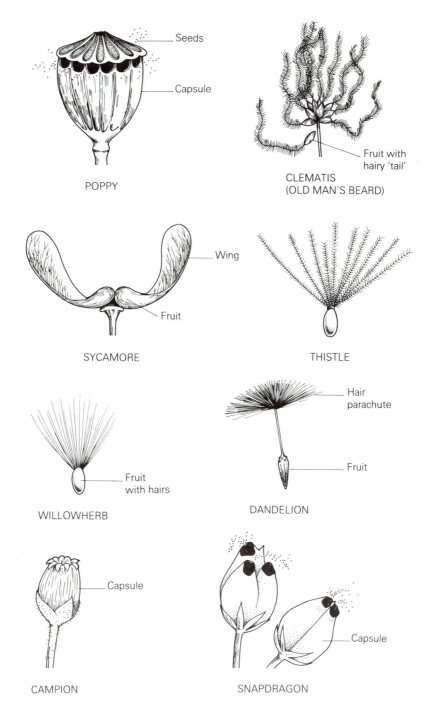

Figure 5.10 Some wind-dispersed seeds

99

Animal-dispersed seeds

Animals disperse seeds in two ways. The fruits may have hooks which cling to animals' fur. You may have seen the small green fruits of goose grass or cleavers clinging to your trousers or socks after running through long grass or undergrowth. Other hooked fruits are produced by burdock and agrimony. Chickweed and plantain do not have hooks, but their seeds become sticky when wet and they cling on to fur until they dry out again.

Many fruits are eaten by animals and the seeds, which are protected, pass through the animal's digestive system and are passed out with their droppings. In the apple, the pips are the seeds, and the part that we eat is formed from the receptacle of the apple flower which has grown around the seeds. The strawberry is also a swollen receptacle, but the seeds in their ovaries are the tiny pips on the outside. In plums the outside part of the ovary becomes fleshy and nice to eat, while the inside part forms a hard 'store'. The seed is inside this store. Blackberries are rather like collections of tiny plums, except that the store inside is soft and not hard like the plum. (See Figure 5.11.)

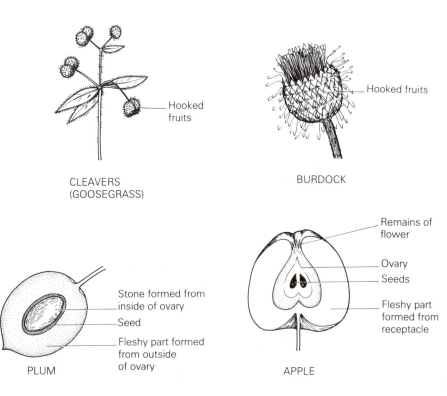

CLEAVERS
(GOOSEGRASS)

BURDOCK

PLUM

APPLE

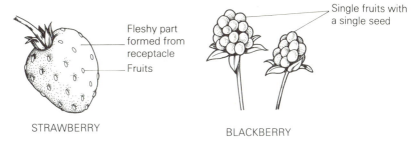

Fleshy part formed from receptacle

Fruits

STRAWBERRY

Single fruits with a single seed

BLACKBERRY

Figure 5.11   Some animal-dispersed seeds

Self-dispersed seeds

In some plants the ovary splits open suddenly and throws the seeds out. These are called *self-dispersed* seeds. The plants in which this happens include the pea and sweet pea, the wallflower, lupin and gorse. The splitting is caused by the ovary drying out and becoming tensed. Suddenly the strain becomes too much and the ovary bursts open. On a warm summer day you can easily hear the popping of gorse fruits as they split. (See Figure 5.12.)

Pods ready to split

Pod split open

Seeds

GORSE

SWEET PEA

Figure 5.12   Some self-dispersed seeds

5.6 Germination

When the seed begins to grow in the ground it is said to *germinate*. Once the plant has started to grow out of the seed it is called a *seedling*, which grows up and out of the ground. Once the plant is in the light, it can photosynthesise and grow much more quickly.

A seed has its own food store but still will not germinate unless conditions are right. In the next experiments you will investigate the conditions necessary for germination.

Investigating the conditions needed for germination

1. Write down your hypothesis for what conditions may be needed. This experiment may not investigate all the things you think may be important. Once you have set up this experiment you may want to design further experiments of your own. Design them and then check with your teacher whether you can do them.

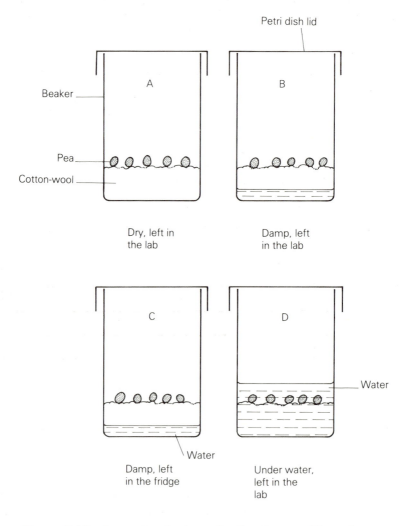

Figure 5.13   Apparatus for investigating the conditions for germination

2. Take four beakers labelled A, B, C and D, some cotton-wool, 20 peas, two Petri dishes and some distilled water. Label the beakers with your group initials.

3. Treat the beakers as follows:

    Beaker A. Put some dry cotton-wool in the bottom of the beaker and five peas on top of the cotton-wool. Cover the beaker with a Petri dish or lid as in the diagram, and leave in a warm place in the lab.

    Beaker B. Put some wet cotton-wool in the beaker with five peas on it. Add some more water until it just comes to the bottom of the cotton-wool. Put a Petri dish or lid on and leave in a warm place next to beaker A.

    Beaker C. Treat this exactly the same as B but put it in the fridge.

    Beaker D. Put wet cotton-wool in the beaker with five peas. Add more water until the peas are completely covered. Put a lid on and leave next to beakers A and B. (See Figure 5.13.)

4. Leave the beakers for a week and then check to see which peas had germinated. Write down the results in a table:

Beaker	*Peas germinated*	*Reason why peas did or did not germinate*
A		
B		
C		
D		

5. What conditions do you think are necessary for germination? Was your hypothesis correct?

Germination success

Even under the best conditions, not all seeds will germinate. It is not really possible to say why, it just seems that not every seed is able to grow. The next experiment investigates the germination success rate for cress.

Investigating germination success

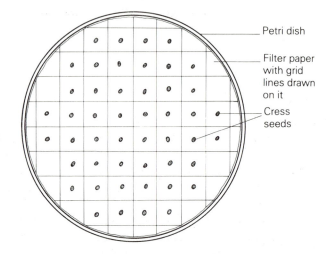

Figure 5.14   Apparatus for investigating germination

1. Take a clean piece of filter paper and a Petri dish. Using the dish as your guide, draw a circle on the filter paper and cut it out so that it exactly fits the dish.

2. Using a sharp pencil, draw a series of faint lines exactly 1 cm apart across the whole of the circle of filter paper. Turn the paper round and draw a second series of lines to make a grid of squares 1 cm × 1 cm (see Figure 5.14). This will give you at least 50 squares.

3. Put the filter paper into the dish and wet it. Be careful not to flood the dish.

4. Take 50 cress seeds and carefully put one seed into each square until you have used up all the seeds.

5. Label the lid with your group initials and put it on to the dish. Leave the dish in a warm place for a few days.

6. Count the number of seeds which did not germinate, and count or work out the number of seeds which did.

7. To find the percentage of seeds which germinated (percentage means the number out of 100) multiply the number of seeds which germinated by two.

8. In your conclusion write down the percentage of seeds which germinated. This is called the *germination success rate*.

5.7 Growing a seedling

Even though we can do many experiments on growing plants, and we understand much about how they work, the growth of a seedling is still a very wonderful process. To watch it in detail you will be growing a broad bean seed because this is large and produces a large plant. While growing the seed you must do a number of things to learn as much as you can. In particular you must check your seedling every day to make sure that it does not dry out and die. Figure 5.15 is a labelled diagram of a broad bean seedling. You will have to draw your seedling as it grows. Try to make your drawing simple and clear and use the labels from this figure on your drawings.

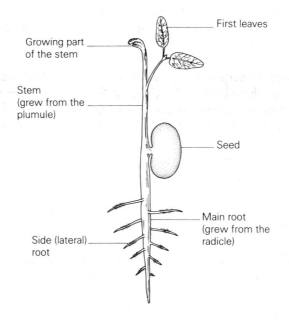

Figure 5.15   A broad bean seedling

Growing a bean

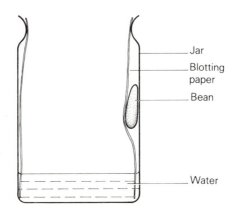

Figure 5.16   How to grow a broad bean

1. Take a tall clean jam jar, some paper towels or blotting paper, and a bean which has been soaked in water for 24 hours (see Figure 5.16).

2. Roll the paper towels into a tube which just fits inside the jam jar.

3. Soak the paper towel thoroughly and leave about 1 cm of water in the bottom of the jar.

4. Wedge the bean in between the paper towel and the jar, about half way down the jar.

5. Each group of four pupils should set up another jar with a bean in, for another part of this experiment.

6. Put your beans in a warm light place and remember to check them every day. Water them when necessary.

7. There will be a number of results for this experiment. You will have to leave several pages in your book to keep them all together.

8. Copy out a table like the one below:

Day	Length of radicle/mm	Length of plumule/mm	Total length of seedling/mm
1			
2			
3			
↓ 20			

9. Each day measure the length of the radicle and plumule and write them down. Until they appear write 0 mm.

10. Every three days make a simple, labelled sketch of your seedling.

11. Have you ever wondered why plants always grow upwards out of the ground? When the spare seedling is between 60 and 80 mm long, carefully take it out of the jar and put it back upside down. Observe how it grows and three days later make a labelled sketch of it.

12. Finally after three weeks, draw graphs of the length of your bean as it grew. Draw three growth lines on the same graph, one for the radicle, one for the plumule and one for the whole plant, as in Figure 5.17.

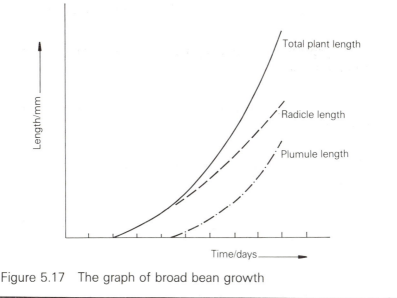

Figure 5.17   The graph of broad bean growth

5.8 Growing plants without seeds

It is not always necessary to sow seeds to grow new plants. Sometimes we can simply cut off a part of a stem and put it into damp soil. It will then grow roots and within a couple of weeks be a complete healthy plant. This is *asexual reproduction*, which does not need male and female parent cells. It is also called *vegetative reproduction*. Once again plants reproduce vegetatively in a number of different ways.

Cuttings

Cuttings are small pieces of stem with some leaves attached which are cut off a healthy plant. The cut stems are placed in water or damp soil, and within two weeks they produce roots. Many house plants are swapped by this method. Someone takes a cutting from a friend's plant and gives a different one in return—each gets another plant at no extra cost. Sometimes to speed up root growth a substance called *rooting compound* may be added to the cut stems or water.

Grafts

Grafts are used particularly with fruit trees and rose bushes. A cut is made into a stem of a tree or bush and a small stem with buds from another similar tree or bush is trimmed and fitted into the cut. The two are bound together and sealed in, and within a few weeks they will have grown together (see Figure 5.18). The fruit or rose flower which grows from the graft will have some features of both the original plants.

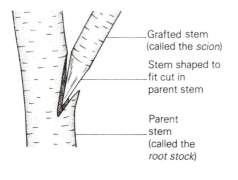

Grafted stem
(called the *scion*)

Stem shaped to
fit cut in
parent stem

Parent
stem
(called the
root stock)

Joint bound
with greaseproof
paper and
twine

Figure 5.18   How to grow a graft

Growing cuttings

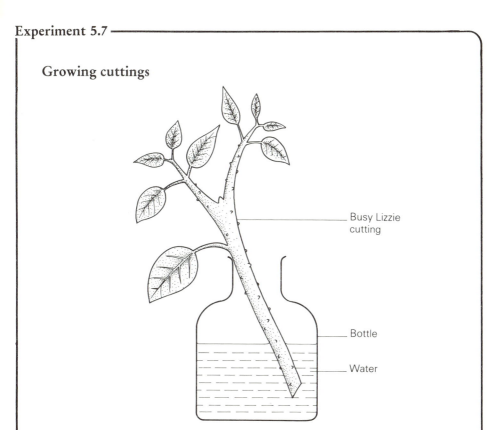

Busy Lizzie
cutting

Bottle

Water

Figure 5.19   How to grow a cutting

1. Using a sharp knife cut off a piece of stem from a busy Lizzie or geranium or other similar house plant.

2. Stand the cutting in a small bottle with water in (see Figure 5.19).

3. Time how many days it takes for roots to appear.

4. Once the cutting has grown healthy roots, plant it in a pot with some compost. Be careful not to damage the roots.

Bulbs, corms and tubers

These are all swollen parts of roots or stems which will grow into a new plant. The onion is a bulb, and the potato is a tuber. Gardeners will grow onions from seed or from sets, which are young onion plants grown from seed. In this way we grow onions for eating. To grow onion seed we need to plant the onion itself. Seed potatoes are not seeds at all but ordinary potatoes grown specially for planting. They grow much more quickly to produce a crop than real potato seed. However, all potatoes can be used as 'seed' potatoes.

Experiment 5.8

Growing an onion

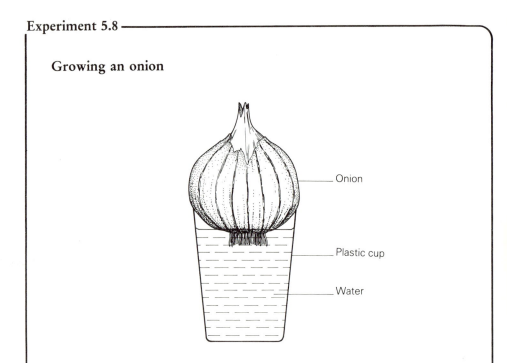

Figure 5.20   Growing an onion

1. Take an onion and a clean plastic disposable cup or yoghurt pot.

2. Fill the cup with water and put the onion on to the rim of the cup so that its base is just in the water (see Figure 5.20). You may have to cut the cup to a suitable size.

3. Observe the roots growing over the next few days. If left long enough, the onion will produce a shoot.

Growing a potato

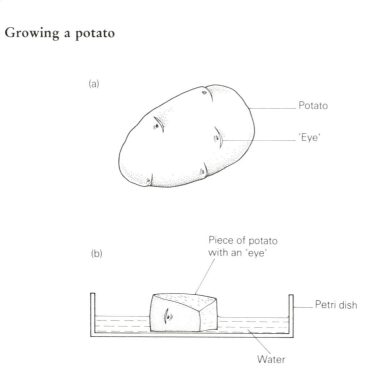

Figure 5.21   Growing a potato

1. Take a potato and cut out of it a simple 'eye' with some of the potato still attached (see Figure 5.21(a)).

2. Label a Petri dish or its lid with your initials and put the cut piece of potato in the dish with some water (see Figure 5.21(b)).

3. Leave this in a warm place but check each day to make sure the potato does not dry out.

4. After a while you should see a shoot growing from the 'eye.'

Figure 5.22   Strawberry runners

Runners   Plants like the strawberry produce long thin runners which grow from their stems (see Figure 5.22). These runners grow roots and stems at different places along the runner producing lots more plants.

Spores and others

Plants like yeast will reproduce either by one cell simply dividing into two new smaller cells (this is called *fission*) or they can divide into lots of very tiny cells with a hard outer covering, called spores. As we have seen in Chapter 4, these spores will grow into new colonies if conditions are right.

Single-celled animals also reproduce asexually by fission.

Questions on Chapter 5

Fill in the missing words from the following sentences.

1. _____ reproduction is where a _____ cell joins with a _____ cell. This is called _____, and in plants the _____ cell is the pollen and the _____ cell is the ovule. _____ reproduction needs only one parent plant.

2. There are two forms of pollination: _____ and _____ pollination. _____ pollination is where pollen from one plant fertilises the ovule of another.

3. When the pollen lands on the _____, a _____ liquid causes the pollen grain to split and produce a _____. This

grows into the stigma and _____ of the plant and down to the
_____, where its nucleus joins with the _____ nucleus.

4. A plant seed is made of two parts: the _____ which will grow
into the new plant, and its _____.

5. Give the names of five foods which are made from plant seeds. Write
down the plants that the seeds come from.

6. Write down the conditions necessary for seeds to germinate. How do
you think a farmer would make sure that the wheat seeds he plants
will have the right conditions?

7. In two experiments to grow peas, out of 25 seeds planted 20 grew in
the first experiment and 22 in the second. What was the percentage
success in each case? What was the average percentage success for
peas?

Crossword on Chapter 5

Across

1 Seeds do this before they start to 7 down (9)

6 24 across tubes can be grown in a _____ solution (5)

8 An onion and tulip both reproduce using these (5)

11 Seeds can be dispersed by the _____ (4)

14 Plant with hooked fruits (10)

16 A source of energy for plants (3)

17 Reproduction with only one parent is _____ (7)

18 Part of a seed which will grow into the root (7)

19 Corn on the cob comes from _____ plants (5)

21 A dandelion parachute is made of this (4)

22 Tree with winged fruit (8)

24 and 5 down. An ovule is fertilised by a _____ _____ (6, 5)

25 Spiky plant with an explosive fruit (5)

26 Microbes reproduce by producing these (6)

Down

2 Part of a seed which will become the new plant (6)

3 Stamens are the _____ parts of the flower (4)

4 Sexual reproduction requires _____ cells to make the zygote (3)

5 See 24 across

7 No seed can _____ before fertilisation (4)

9 24 across lands on this to fertilise an ovule (6)

10 Seed _____ is essential if plants are not to crowd each other out (9)

12 Sometimes these pollinate plants (7)

13 Plant with a wind-dispersed fruit (9)

14 It is often used to reproduce rose bushes (5)

15 Reproduction involving two parents is _____ (6)

20 Cell formed after fertilisation (6)

23 Plants and animals need this to survive (3)

24 Seed inside an apple (3)

Trace this grid on to a piece of paper, and then fill in the answers.

6. Growing new animals

6.1 Beginning an animal

Producing animals seems much more complicated than producing plants. We cannot just go out and buy packets of animal seed to sow. In fact, however, the way that animals reproduce is very similar to the way that plants do. Plants need pollen from the male part of the flower and an ovule from the female part. Animals, too, usually need a male cell from the father and a female cell from the mother. This is the same as saying that most plants and animals use *sexual reproduction*. Some animals can reproduce asexually but we will look at these at the end of the chapter.

One of the main differences between how animals reproduce and how plants do is that animal cells cannot survive being dried out at any stage during reproduction. In fact even adult animals will quickly die if they do not get enough water. Plants, however, are able to cope quite well with low amounts of water. Plant pollen has a protective coat which stops the cell inside from drying out. Plant embryo — that is, seeds — can have almost no water at all and can survive for between two and twenty years.

Animal reproduction is therefore adapted to make sure that the male cell, the female cell and the embryo never dry out, and, as you will see, many animals have quite complex reproductive systems which help prevent this from happening.

Most animals, too, have separate males and females but some can be male and female at the same time. The common earthworm is like this and so too is the snail. Animals like these two have both the male and female reproductive organs.

Reproductive organs

The reproductive organs are all the parts of an animal or plant which are concerned with reproduction. This includes not only the parts which actually make the male and female cells, but also the parts which store them and the parts which are used to bring male and female cells together. The next exercise will remind you of the plant reproductive organs, and as you read the chapter you will learn about the different sort of animal reproductive organs.

The male cell

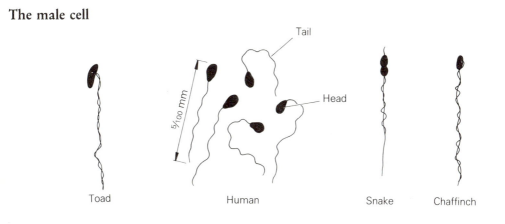

Figure 6.1   Sperm of different animals

In animals the male reproductive cell is called the *sperm*, or *spermatozoa*. Sperms can be quite different from each other but they can all swim, by wiggling their tails. Figure 6.1 shows a number of different sperms. They are all very small, for example a human sperm is about ½₀ of a millimetre long. In air these sperm would die in a few seconds but in the right conditions they can live for two or three days. Sperm are made in organs called *testes*.

The female reproductive cell is shown in Figure 6.2. It is called the *egg* or *ovum*, which you will recognise as being very much like the word ovule for a plant egg. Do not confuse the word *egg* with an egg from a chicken for instance. Although the egg cell is larger than a sperm it is still tiny. A human egg cell measures about ¹⁄₁₀ of a millimetre across. A chicken's egg contains not only the egg cell, or, if it has been fertilised, the embryo, but also a large store of food (the *yolk*) and water for the chick to grow with.

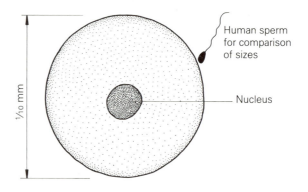

Figure 6.2   A human egg cell

An egg cell cannot swim and has to wait for sperm to swim to it to be fertilised. Egg cells are made in organs called *ovaries*.

Animals face two problems in their reproduction. The first is getting the sperms and the egg to meet without either of them drying out. The second is growing the embryo in a safe place, with enough food and water until it is able to move to get its own food.

6.2 Mating

Mating consists of a male and a female animal coming together in order that the sperm can meet the egg and fertilise it. Most animals mate, even the ones like the worm which has male and female reproductive organs.

Mating has a number of different names. In humans, for example, it is also called *sexual intercourse*, or *copulation* or *making love*.

The ways in which animals mate depend on what sort of animals they are and where they live. We shall look at a number of them.

The earthworm

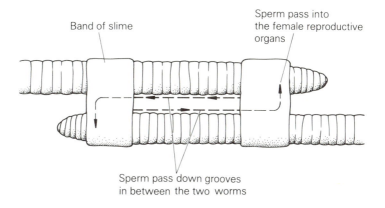

Band of slime

Sperm pass into the female reproductive organs

Sperm pass down grooves in between the two worms

Figure 6.3   Earthworms mating

Two worms mate by lying side by side, but in opposite directions (see Figure 6.3). They are held together by bands of slime produced by the clitella. Sperm are passed out of each worm's testes and squeezed along grooves on the outside of the worm until they pass into the openings to the female reproductive organs of the other worm. Bands of slime around each worm keep the sperms separate and stop them from drying out.

The stickleback

Animals which live in water do not have the problem of their sperms, eggs or embryos drying out. The stickleback male builds a nest using bits of plant stuck together with a glue that he produces. He then entices a female who is full of eggs to lay them in his nest. He pushes and prods her until she has laid the eggs and then chases her out of the nest. He then quickly goes into the nest himself and passes out sperms all over the eggs. The eggs are fertilised and they grow and hatch in the nest, watched over by the male. (See Figure 6.4 over the page.)

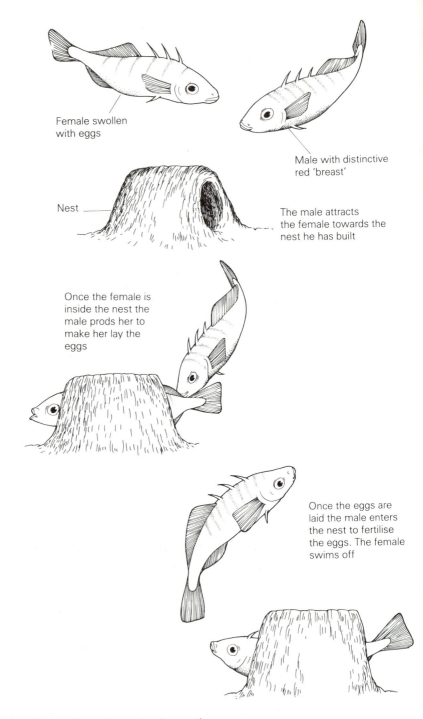

Female swollen
with eggs

Male with distinctive
red 'breast'

Nest

The male attracts
the female towards the
nest he has built

Once the female is
inside the nest the
male prods her to
make her lay the
eggs

Once the eggs are
laid the male enters
the nest to fertilise
the eggs. The female
swims off

Figure 6.4   Sticklebacks mating

Frogspawn is a common sight in ponds and streams in spring (see Figure 6.5). Frogs eggs are just left to hatch by themselves. They will not dry out and are protected from being eaten to some extent because they are inside a large ball of jelly.

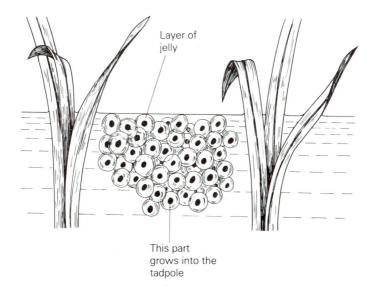

Layer of jelly

This part grows into the tadpole

Figure 6.5   Frogspawn in a reed bed

The actual frog embryo is the black dot in the centre of the spawn, the jelly coat swells up a few seconds after the egg is laid. It is because of this jelly coat that frogs have to behave in a special way during mating. Like the stickleback, there is no problem with the sperm or egg cell drying out, but because the sperm cannot swim through the jelly coat they must fertilise the egg before it swells up.

During the mating season, a male frog will ride on the female's back in a piggy-back fashion (as in Figure 6.6 over the page). He hangs on to the female using special hard pads on his thumbs which grip the female behind her front legs. As soon as she starts to lay egg cells the male sheds sperms into the water and the egg cells are fertilised.

Figure 6.6　Frogs mating

6.3　Mating in Man

Humans, along with all land animals, have to avoid the sperms or the egg cell drying out, and so have developed specialised reproductive organs to make sure this does not happen. Figures 6.7 and 6.8 show the male and female systems as seen from the front of the body. They have been drawn so you can see the insides of the reproductive organs.

The male reproductive organs

Sperm are made in the two testes like in all animals. In mammals the testes hang outside the body in a bag called the *scrotum*, because in mammals the body temperature is a little too high for good sperm production. The testes are kept a little cooler outside the main part of the body. Each testis is connected to the *penis* by a tube called the *sperm duct*. The sperm pass along this tube to be stored in two small containers called the *seminal vesicles*. The penis has a tube running through it which can carry both sperm and urine from the bladder, although not at the same time.

It is not possible to cut open a man to see the reproductive organs. Instead you can look at them in a rat which is very much like a human.

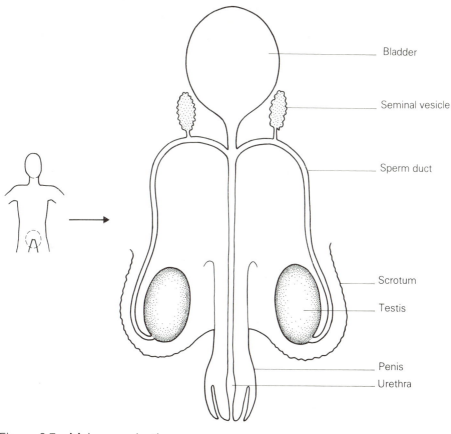

Figure 6.7   Male reproductive organs

Bladder

Seminal vesicle

Sperm duct

Scrotum

Testis

Penis

Urethra

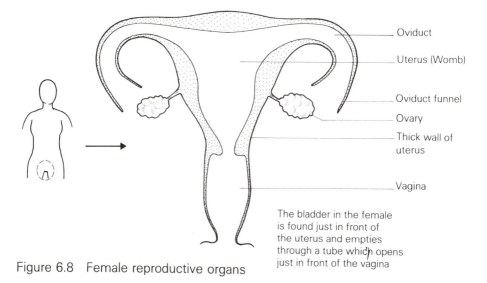

Figure 6.8   Female reproductive organs

Oviduct

Uterus (Womb)

Oviduct funnel

Ovary

Thick wall of uterus

Vagina

The bladder in the female is found just in front of the uterus and empties through a tube which opens just in front of the vagina

Looking at the male reproductive organs in a rat

1. Pin out a male rat (Figure 6.9) on a dissection board.

2. Identify the testes and the penis.

3. Make a cut down the mid-line and peel back the skin.

4. Cut through the abdomen wall and remove it. You can now see the rat's digestive system. Identify the parts.

5. Remove the digestive system and find the bladder.

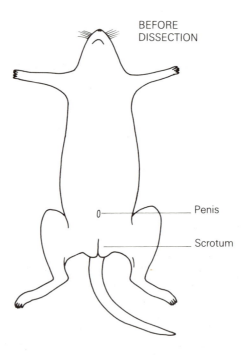

BEFORE DISSECTION

Penis

Scrotum

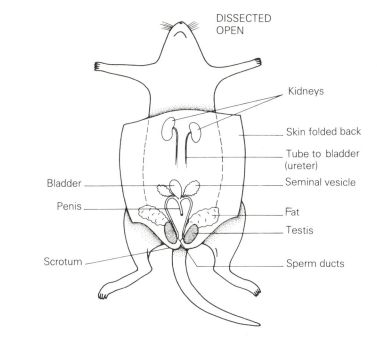

Kidneys

Skin folded back

Tube to bladder (ureter)

Bladder

Seminal vesicle

Penis

Fat

Testis

Scrotum

Sperm ducts

Figure 6.9   The male rat

6. Cut through the skin of the scrotum by one testis and peel it away.

7. With care you should now be able to see the testis, the sperm duct, the bladder and the penis. Can you also see the tube coming from the kidney to the bladder which carries the urine?

The female reproductive organs

Egg cells are made in the two ovaries. They are passed out of the ovary into a tube called the *oviduct* or *egg tube*, which has a funnel at its end to make sure it catches the egg cell.

The egg cell is slowly carried down the oviduct and takes between four and five days to get to the *uterus*, or *womb*. It is in the uterus that the baby will grow if the egg has been fertilised. The uterus connects to the outside of the body by a tube called the *vagina*.

Looking at the female reproductive organs in a rat

1. Pin out a female rat (Figure 6.10) on a dissection board.

2. Identify the entrance to the vagina and the nipples.

3. Make a cut down the mid-line and peel back the skin.

4. Cut through the abdomen wall and remove it. Once again the digestive system is visible. Remove it.

5. You should now be able to see the ovaries and the uterus. They may have lots of white fat around them. Clear this away. Note here that the rat has a much longer uterus than a human because rats usually produce between eight and twelve babies.

6. With care you should be able to see the vagina, but this runs under part of the pelvis bone and may be difficult to see. Try cutting the bone away with heavy scissors.

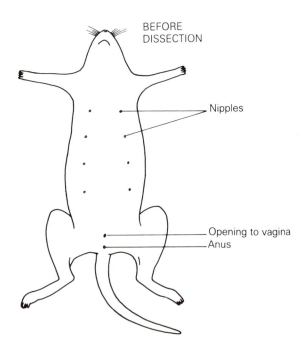

BEFORE
DISSECTION

Nipples

Opening to vagina

Anus

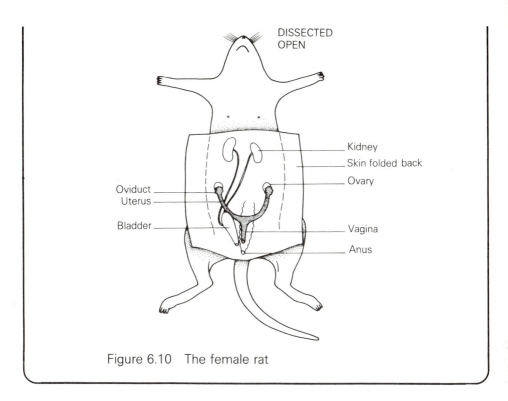

DISSECTED OPEN

Kidney
Skin folded back
Ovary

Oviduct
Uterus

Bladder

Vagina

Anus

Figure 6.10 The female rat

Fertilisation In Man and in the other mammals mating involves putting the penis inside the vagina. This is called *sexual intercourse*. To do this the penis becomes filled with blood which makes it stiff. This is called an *erection*. The penis is placed inside the vagina, and sperm are forced out by powerful muscles in the penis. The sperms will be pushed up and into the uterus. They will then swim in liquid, which covers the inside of all the reproductive tubes, up into the oviduct. They take about an hour to swim all the way. The sperm will stay in the oviduct for about two days by which time they will have died. However, if an egg cell is present, one sperm will fertilise it. In the absence of a sperm the egg cell lives for only two or three days after it is released from the ovary, and because only one egg cell is released each month, intercourse does not always mean an egg will be fertilised.

6.4 Becoming adults

Young people, like all young animals, cannot reproduce and have babies because their reproductive organs do not work. As we grow up they begin to produce eggs or sperm. Once they start they cause other changes in the body, changes like the voice breaking and growing hair on the face in boys and the growth of breasts in girls. These changes are called *puberty* or sometimes *adolescence*. Different people begin puberty at different ages. Some girls may start as early as nine years old whilst others do not begin until they are 14 or even later. The most usual age is around 12. Boys start at between 12 and 15.

The differences between starting ages for puberty may make some youngsters worry because it has not started yet. This is quite normal and is just another of the many differences between people. You must realise that no matter when you start, in the end everybody goes through puberty successfully.

Puberty in boys

One of the first signs of puberty in a boy is a deepening of his voice—his voice 'breaks'. Also hair starts to grow on his chest, under his arms, between his legs, and on his face. Sperm start to be made and are occasionally forced out during the night, during what is called a *wet dream*. This is quite normal. In puberty a boy's shoulders start to get broader. The boy begins to sound like and look like a man. He also becomes more aware of girls.

Puberty in girls

In puberty a girl's breasts start to develop and hair grows under her arms and between her legs. The ovaries start to produce eggs at the rate of about one a month, but this may be very irregular until the cycle has settled down. Along with egg production there are other changes, all of which are part of what is called the *menstrual cycle*. Each month an egg is produced and it slowly passes down the oviduct to the uterus. The uterus, meanwhile, has become much thicker inside. It has produced a soft, spongy surface with lots of blood vessels, ready to receive a fertilised egg. If the egg has not been fertilised, then the dead egg and the lining of the uterus pass out of the body through the vagina. This is called a *period*, and it lasts between three and seven days. A girl will lose a little blood and to absorb it she must wear sanitary towels, changing them often.

Periods may be very irregular at first, and sometimes months go by without a girl having one. They settle down to a cycle of around every 28 days, but this may be as short as 25 days or as long as 35. During a period, and just before it, a girl may feel irritable and off-colour. This is quite normal.

6.5 Growing the baby

In humans the embryo is kept inside the mother for a while. This time is called *pregnancy*, and it happens in all mammals. In humans it takes nine months, but in mice or gerbils it takes only about three weeks. In elephants it lasts for two years.

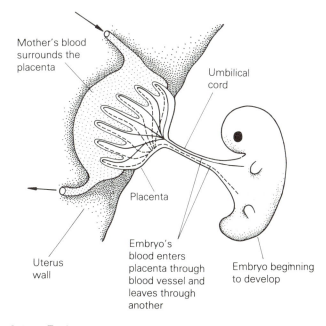

Mother's blood surrounds the placenta

Umbilical cord

Placenta

Uterus wall

Embryo's blood enters placenta through blood vessel and leaves through another

Embryo beginning to develop

Figure 6.11   Embryo and placenta

During pregnancy the baby is growing, it is warm and of course it cannot dry out. It has lots of food which it gets from its mother. As the baby grows it is enclosed in a bag which is full of water. This stops the baby from being bumped around as the mother moves. The baby is connected by a tube called the umbilical cord to the *placenta*. This is the part which joins the baby to the mother's uterus. At the placenta the baby's blood and the mother's blood come very close together, so that food and oxygen can pass from the mother's blood to the baby's. Wastes pass from the baby's blood to the mother's. (See Figure 6.11.)

It is important that the mother's blood does not actually mix with the baby's because harmful substances could pass into the baby. As it is, nicotine and alcohol can pass across the placenta into the baby's blood, which is why pregnant women should not smoke at all or drink much alcohol.

129

You can get some idea of what an embryo is like by looking inside a rat which is pregnant.

Demonstration Experiment 6.3

Looking at rat embryos

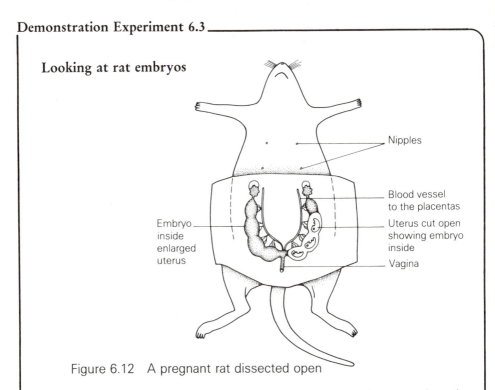

Figure 6.12   A pregnant rat dissected open

1. Pin out a pregnant female rat (Figure 6.12) on to a dissection board.

2. Notice how much larger the rat is than the normal female. The nipples are more visible.

3. Carefully dissect open the rat as in Experiment 6.2.

4. Observe how the embryos have pushed the digestive system to one side. Remove the digestive system.

5. Count the number of embryos. Observe the placenta for each one. What is it like?

6. Cut out the uterus between each embryo and remove the embryo and uterus.

7. Working in groups take an embryo in a Petri dish and a pair of forceps. Carefully remove the membranes from around the embryo.

8. Measure and sketch your embryo.

As the embryo grows, it changes shape so that by about two months it looks like a baby and is about 3 cm long. By the time it is three months it is about 4½ cm long and is completely organised into a baby. It then grows for the next six months until it is ready to be born. Figure 6.13 shows some of the changes the embryo goes through.

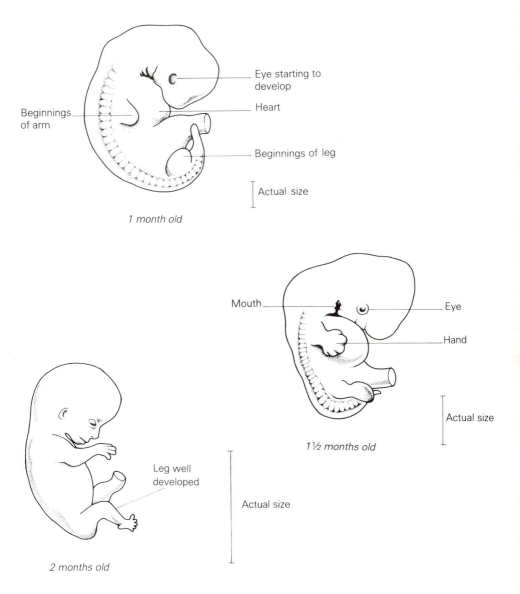

Figure 6.13 Part of the development of an embryo

From about the fourth month onward the baby may start to move its arms and legs but later it may move around in the uterus. The mother is able to feel her baby moving, often being gently kicked from the inside.

6.6 Birth

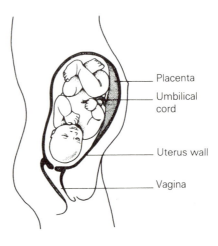

Figure 6.14   The baby turns upside down ready to be born

After about nine months the baby will move in the uterus so that it is upside down, as in Figure 6.14. The mother will have felt her tummy muscles 'practising', ready to push the baby out, occasionally for several weeks. These muscles tighten up and the membranes around the baby burst. Gradually the entrance to the uterus and the vagina open up to let the baby through, and at the same time the tummy muscles start to push more frequently. This whole time is called *labour* and may last between six and 24 hours. Eventually the baby is pushed out head first into the world. There is always a doctor or midwife present when a baby is born, and he or she will support the baby as it is being born and will cut the umbilical cord once the baby is out. (See Figure 6.15.) Very quickly the baby will cry, not because it is in pain but this is just the air coming out after it has taken its very first breath.

Shortly after the baby is born the placenta and umbilical cord will be pushed out of the uterus. This is called the *after-birth*. The uterus then relaxes and the mother can get her first rest for several hours.

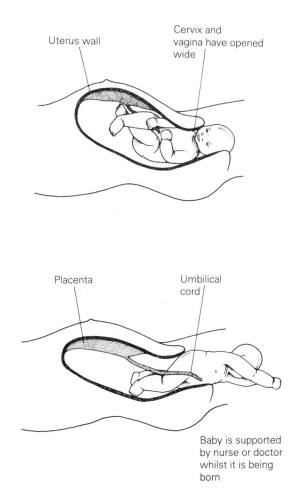

Uterus wall

Cervix and vagina have opened wide

Placenta

Umbilical cord

Baby is supported by nurse or doctor whilst it is being born

Figure 6.15   The birth of a baby

6.7 Growing children

After the baby is born it is completely dependent on its mother. For the first few months all it appears to do is feed and sleep. Gradually it gets stronger so that by the time it is about a year old it has developed in many ways including beginning to walk. Even so it still needs lots of care and love from its mother and father for many years, gradually learning and developing until it is able to take care of itself.

Other animals need to be cared for too. The stickleback father looks after the babies. Frogs, of course, do not look after the tadpoles at all; they have to fend for themselves. Animals like horses have to stand up within a few hours of being born, otherwise they would not be able to get their mother's milk. Human babies stay with their parents for much longer than other animals do. This is because humans have to develop and learn much more than other animals.

You could do a project on how babies grow up. You can find out what sort of food they eat and what sort of things they can do at different ages.

6.8 Growing tadpoles

You may keep pets which have had babies or you may have a younger brother or sister who you have watched growing up. Usually it takes a long time to watch animals growing, but tadpoles grow quite quickly and are easy to keep. You can keep them in a fish tank. If it's a small one, you may need an aerator to supply enough oxygen. You also need a little weed for the tadpoles to feed on, and once they have become frogs they need a sloping rock to be able to climb out on. (See Figure 6.16.)

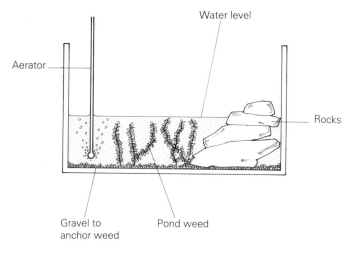

Figure 6.16   A tank suitable for growing tadpoles in

Growing tadpoles

1. Collect some frogspawn and set up a tank as just described.

2. Keep a diary of the development of the frogspawn.

3. Every two days remove one embryo and put it into a watch glass. Use a hand lens to see its shape. Make a clear sketch of it.

4. Once the tadpoles have hatched make sketches every week to show how they are growing. It takes about three months after the tadpole hatches for it to start to become a frog. The change to a frog, called *metamorphosis*, takes four weeks.

5. Once metamorphosis has happened, the frog will need insect larvae to eat. You can supply these by putting stream or pond water into the tank. Eventually though you will have to let the frogs go by releasing them to a pond or stream.

6.9 Asexual reproduction in animals

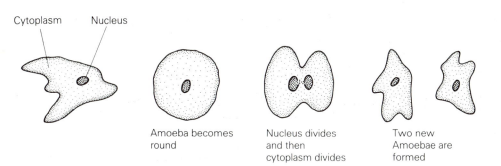

Cytoplasm   Nucleus

Amoeba becomes round

Nucleus divides and then cytoplasm divides

Two new Amoebae are formed

Figure 6.17   Simple division in an Amoeba

Only some animals can reproduce like this. Single-celled animals, like an Amoeba, simply divide into two (see Figure 6.17). Animals like starfish and flatworms can be cut into pieces, and each piece will then grow again into a new animal. There is a story that oyster fishermen were worried because starfish were living in the oyster beds, eating the oysters. Each time a fisherman caught a starfish he would chop it into pieces and throw it back into the water. Of course this did not cure the fishermen's problem; it only made it worse.

It is not true that if a worm is chopped in half it will grow into a new worm. The worm has most of its important organs in its front half and if not too much is chopped off, a front part will be able to grow a new part. A back part cannot grow a new front.

Questions on Chapter 6

Fill in the missing words in the following sentences.

1. An animal male reproductive cell is called a _____ and is made in an organ called the _____.

2. An animal female reproductive cell is called an _____ or an _____ and is made in an organ called the _____.

3. _____ is where a male and a female animal come together so that the _____ can swim to the _____ and fertilise it.

4. In humans, the male reproductive organs consist of two _____ joined by tubes to the _____. The _____ hang outside the body in a bag called the scrotum because sperm production works best at a _____ temperature.

5. In humans the female reproductive organs consist of two _____ connected by tubes to the _____. This is connected to the outside by a tube called the _____. The _____ is the place that the baby will grow in and is also called the _____.

6. In humans eggs are produced about once a month in a cycle called the _____ cycle. If the egg is not fertilised, then it and the _____ of the uterus are released out through the _____. This is called the _____, and it lasts between three and seven days.

7. The time when a baby is growing inside its mother is called _____. In humans it lasts for about _____ months and then the baby is born. The time of birth is called _____, and

there is a doctor or midwife with the mother to make sure that the birth goes properly. The baby is usually born _____ first still attached to the mother by the _____ cord. A little while after the baby is born the placenta is pushed out of the uterus. This is called the _____ .

8. Find out how long pregnancy takes in animals like dogs, cats, mice and elephants. When you have made a list of eight to ten animals draw a bar graph to compare their pregnancy times.

Crossword on Chapter 6

Across

1 This attaches a baby to its mother in the uterus (8)

4 The baby passes these from his blood to his mother's (6)

7 A male stickleback _____ the female to make her lay her eggs (5)

8 Female reproductive organs (7)

10, 19. Long tube which attaches a baby to his mother (9, 4)

12 It is used in bands to hold two worms together (5)

13 Plants and animals will die without it (5)

16 A baby gets this from his mother (4)

18 It is laid by frogs (9)

19 See 10 across

21 Change between young boy and man or young girl and woman (7)

23 It passes from the mother to the baby in the uterus (6)

26 See 24 down

28, 29. It connects each 5 down to the penis (5, 4)

29 See 28

Down

2 An animal which becomes round and reproduces by dividing (6) . . .

3 . . . and producing _____ new animals (3)

5 Male reproductive organ (6)

6 It helps the sperm to 25 down (4)

9 Time between fertilisation and birth (9)

10 A womb (6)

11 Period leading up to the time of birth (6)

14 The cry of a new-born baby is the sound of the first _____ coming out of its lungs (3)

15 A human _____ cell is about ¹⁄₁₀ of a millimetre across (3)

17 Boys begin to grow this on face and chest (4)

20 Males and females have different reproductive _____ (6)

22 In a *period* a girl loses a little _____ (5)

23 Another name for 15 down (4)

24, 26 across. The normal length of 9 down for a woman (4, 6)

25 Sperm do this to get up the oviducts (4)

27 The inside of a man's body would be a little too _____ for good sperm production (3)

Trace this grid on to a piece of paper, and then fill in the answers.

7. How animals feed

7.1 Why eat?

If asked 'Why eat?', we would say we eat to stay alive. What we really mean is that we eat for three different reasons: (a) we eat to get the energy our brain, muscles and nerves need to work; (b) we eat to grow, to make new cells, to make bones, teeth etc.; (c) we eat to repair parts of our body which break or wear out. Cuts or broken bones are obvious examples of this, but also our blood cells live for only about 120 days and are then replaced. Our bodies make about 250 000 million new blood cells each day, or about 2.3 million each second.

To do these three jobs we only need three different sorts of food substances: (a) those which give energy; (b) those which can be used to make cells and tissues; and (c) those which help to keep our whole body working correctly. If you think of your body like a machine, it needs a supply of energy, a stock of spares for building and repair and a drop of oil here and there to keep it running smoothly (see Figure 7.1).

Figure 7.1 The 'body machine'

If you were asked to write a list of the different kinds of food you eat, you could probably write pages and pages. You could probably sort them out into the ones you like and the ones you are told are good for you. But how do you sort them into the three sorts of foods your body needs? Happily 'Nature' has already sorted them out for us into groups and we can test for many of them with simple experiments. You must realise, however, that what we generally call *a* food, like potatoes or steak or biscuits, may in fact contain several of the groups of food types (see Figure 7.2 over the page).

You can see that the word food has two meanings, its everyday meaning and its scientific meaning. To help you we will always use the words *food type* for the scientific meaning.

7.2 Food types

There are only seven food types in nature: *carbohydrates, fats, proteins, minerals, vitamins, water* and *roughage*.

Carbohydrates

Carbohydrates are energy foods, and we eat lots of them. They include the sugars, of which ordinary sugar is only one. There are many other sugars. The most common food we eat is also a carbohydrate. It is called *starch* and is a white substance. Potatoes, rice and bread are almost completely made of starch.

Fats

Fats are also energy foods and are used by animals as a way of storing energy so that there is always some spare, if food is not available. Fat is a white, greasy substance found in many places in animals' bodies but particularly in a layer under the skin. This is because fat also helps to keep heat in. Animals from cold places often have very thick layers of fat or blubber.

Proteins

Proteins are substances used to make cells and living materials for cells. They are complicated substances which we get by eating cells of other organisms. Our bodies are made largely of proteins.

Minerals

Minerals are needed to help make certain parts of the body. They are usually needed only in small amounts but growing animals will often need more. We get all the minerals we need by eating a varied diet containing eggs, milk, meat, vegetables and fruit. The main minerals needed are shown in Table 7.1 on p. 143.

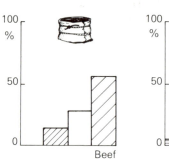

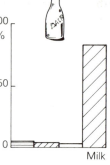

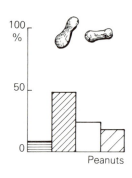

Beef

Milk

Peanuts

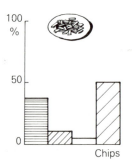

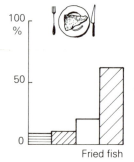

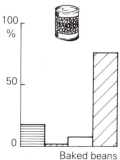

Chips

Fried fish

Baked beans

Eggs

Bread

Apples

Carbohydrate   Fat   Protein   Water

Figure 7.2   What different foods contain

142

Table 7.1 The minerals we need	
Mineral	*What it is used for*
Calcium	In bones and teeth
Iron	In blood cells
Salt (sodium chloride)	In blood and also to make nerves work properly
Phosphorus	In bones and teeth, and also forms part of a substance in the nucleus of all cells
Potassium Magnesium	Help to make muscles work
Copper Manganese	Needed for body growth
Iodine	Needed by thyroid gland to make a chemical which helps control the body

Vitamins   Vitamins are very complicated substances which are used in tiny amounts. They help in many of the vital chemical reactions which go on inside our bodies all the time. Without them certain parts do not work so well and not having the right vitamins may cause serious illness. Such illnesses are called *deficiency diseases*. As with minerals, we get most of our vitamins by eating different foods. Vitamins can, however, be destroyed by our cooking so it is important not to overcook green vegetables. To get our vitamins we should also include fresh foods in our diet, such as milk, cheese and fresh fruit.

Some of the vitamins and their uses are included in Table 7.2 below:

Table 7.2 The vitamins we need	
Vitamin	*Its job and deficiency disease*
A	Helps us to see at night. Keeps the skin moist and healthy. Without it we may suffer night blindness and much skin infection. Eyes, too, can dry out.
B_1 (thiamine)	Important in respiration, that is in getting energy from food. Lack of Vitamin B_1 causes beriberi, a common disease in the Far East, caused by eating a diet mainly of rice. People with beriberi become paralysed if not treated.
Other B Vitamins (riboflavin, niacin)	All used in respiration.
C	Its actual job is not well understood but a lack of it causes scurvy, a disease common among olden-day sailors. It is easily cured by eating oranges, lemons or limes (citrus fruits).
D	Needed to make strong bones in children. Lack of it causes rickets, where the leg bones bend outwards under the weight of the growing child. This vitamin is made in the skin by sunlight and rickets was common among children in cities who were kept indoors a lot.

Water   We are nearly three-quarters water, and it is a vital substance. As you read earlier we would quickly die without it. It helps to keep the whole body working.

Roughage   Roughage is also called *fibre*, and it consists mainly of plant cell material. It seems to help to keep the digestive system healthy, and it also helps to keep food moving inside the digestive system. A lack of fibre can lead to the lower part of the digestive system becoming blocked, called *constipation*.

The food tests

In this experiment, you should simply try the tests to make sure you can do them and can recognise when they have worked. Later you can try them on some foods.

For each test, step 1. involves using a substance which will make the test work. Do each test separately and use clean apparatus each time.

Test for simple sugars

1. Take a test-tube and add four drops of glucose solution.

2. Add about 2 cm³ of blue Benedict's solution.

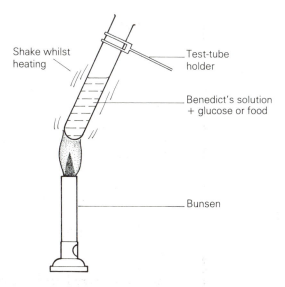

Figure 7.3   A test for simple sugar

3. Warm the mixture gently over a Bunsen flame. Carefully shake the test-tube all the time (see Figure 7.3), otherwise the hot liquid will blow out of the tube. If this happens, wipe up any spilled liquid immediately.

4. Look for a colour change to orange/yellow which shows simple sugar is present. This may take a few seconds to appear. A change to green shows that only a tiny amount (trace) of simple sugar is present.

Test for starch

1. Take a clean white tile and add 3 or 4 drops of starch solution.

2. Add 2 or 3 drops of orange/brown iodine solution (see Figure 7.4).

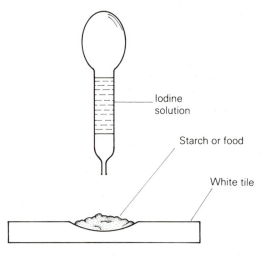

Figure 7.4   A test for starch

3. Look for a colour change to blue/black which shows that starch is present.

Tests for fats (do both)

First test

1. Add a drop of olive oil to a dry test-tube.

2. Add about 2 cm³ of ethanol (alcohol) and shake gently.

3. Put about 2 cm³ of water into a second test-tube.

4. Carefully pour only the clear alcohol from the first tube into the second.

5. Look for a white milky or cloudy appearance when the two liquids mix. This shows fats present. (See Figure 7.5.)

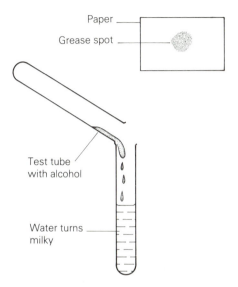

Figure 7.5   Two tests for fats

Second test

1. Take a drop of olive oil on the end of a glass rod.

2. Touch it on to a piece of paper.

3. Hold the paper up to the light. Look for a grease spot which shows fat present.

Test for protein

1. Take a peanut and crush it well in a mortar and pestle. This test will not work unless the food is well crushed.

2. Add about 2 cm^3 of sodium hydroxide and mix.

3. Add 4 or 5 drops of blue copper sulphate solution by dropping them down the inside of the test-tube (see Figure 7.6).

4. Look for a colour change to violet where the two liquids mix. This shows protein present.

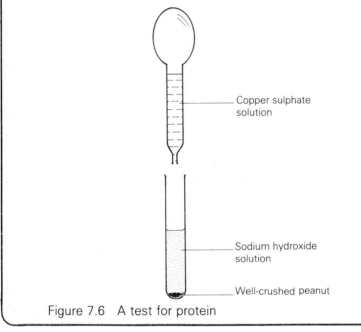

Figure 7.6 A test for protein

Experiment 7.2

Using the food tests to analyse some common foods

1. Take a small amount of a common food like bread or milk or peas.

2. Carefully do each of the four food tests to see what food types it contains. Follow the instructions in Experiment 7.1. In step 1 use the food you are analysing for each test instead of the substances you used before.

3. Record your results in a table like the one below. Use √ or × to show what the food contains.

Food	Simple sugar	Starch	Fats	Protein
e.g. Bread				

4. Repeat this for as many different foods as you can.

In Chapter 5 we said that plant seeds needed to contain food for the growing seedling. In the following experiment you can test to see what sort of food types seeds contain.

Experiment 7.3

Testing the food stores of seeds

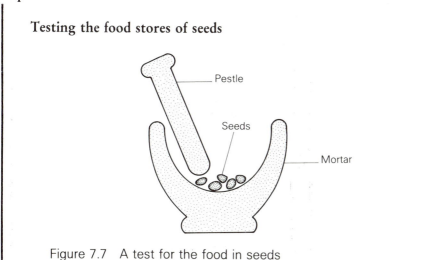

Figure 7.7   A test for the food in seeds

1. Take a range of seeds.

2. Crush some seeds of the same type in a mortar and pestle (Figure 7.7) and test it using each of the four food tests.

3. Record your results in a table as in Experiment 7.2.

4. Repeat using a different seed.

5. What food types do plants need most of?

7.3 Eating the right foods

You can see that if you ate only chips or rice, you would not get all the substances necessary to keep you healthy. Chips contain starch and fats (from the cooking oil) which will give you energy. There will also be a little protein, but what about vitamins and minerals? To make sure that you get all the substances you need it is important to eat lots of different foods. This is called having a *balanced diet*.

The word *diet* means 'all the food we eat'. Often we talk about going on a diet but what we really mean is going on a slimming diet. This is one which has less fats and carbohydrates, because if we eat too much of these our bodies store the extra as fat. Even the carbohydrates are turned into fats. People on a slimming diet must still eat enough protein and vitamins and minerals, and of course enough carbohydrate to give them energy.

A balanced diet means having enough of everything but not too much. To get fat by over-eating can be as bad as to not eat enough. Children especially suffer from not having a balanced diet, and there are many places in the world where you can see children who have not grown properly. They may have rickets giving them bent legs; or swollen tummies because they have not enough of anything. They may be much smaller than children in Britain of the same age, and sometimes they die.

You could do a short project to find out more about what not having a balanced diet means.

Experiment 7.4

Finding the energy value of foods

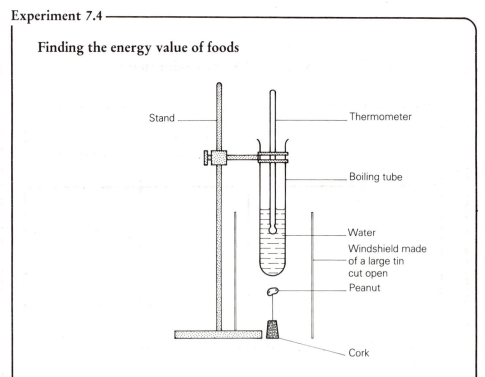

Figure 7.8   Apparatus to measure the energy value of foods

1. Assemble the apparatus shown in Figure 7.8.

2. Put exactly 10 cm^3 of water in the boiling tube.

3. Take the temperature of the water and record it in a table like the one below.

4. Take a peanut and cut it until you have a piece weighing 0.5 g. Stick the piece of peanut on to the pin in the cork.

5. Using a splint set fire to the peanut and quickly put it inside the wind shield under the boiling tube.

6. Allow the nut to burn and take the temperature of the water. Make sure your thermometer does not rest against the sides of the tube.

7. When the peanut has completely burned note the highest temperature reached by the water. Record this.

8. Repeat with fresh water and 0.5 g of another substance.

Food	Temperature at start/°C	Temperature at end/°C	Temperature rise/°C
Peanut			

9. Which 0.5 g piece of food provided the most energy and which the least?

7.4 What happens to the food—digestion

We put food into our mouths, chew it a little and swallow it. What happens to the food is called *digestion*, and, in fact, it begins as soon as food is put into our mouths. Digestion is a way of getting all the substances we need from the food we eat. If you look back to Figure 7.2, you will see that a peanut contains fats, carbohydrates and protein. To separate these substances it is necessary to take the peanut apart, and this process begins with us chewing the peanut into small pieces. This is the first stage of digestion. (See Figure 7.9.)

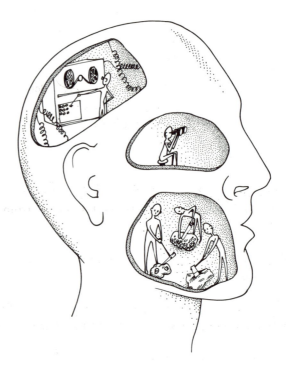

Figure 7.9   Taking food apart — chewing

7.5 Teeth

By the age of 13 or 14 we usually have most of our adult teeth. These are the only adult teeth we will ever get and so it is important to look after them. We have different sorts of teeth, some for biting and some for chewing. In the following experiment you will try to see how many teeth you have got.

Looking at teeth

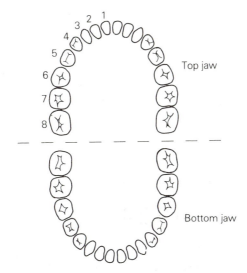

Figure 7.10   A tooth plan

1. Trace or copy the tooth plan in Figure 7.10. It shows the most teeth you could have. The teeth are numbered from the middle of the front, 1 – 8, on each side.

2. Run your tongue around your mouth to count your teeth. Shade in any teeth you have not got.

3. Working in pairs, take a dental mirror which has been sterilised in dilute antiseptic. Use the mirror to look into your partner's mouth.

4. Check that your partner has filled in his/her dental plan correctly with the missing teeth. Can you see the different sorts of teeth?

5. Draw dots on the plan where your parter has had any fillings.

6. Sterilise the mirror again and swap over so that your partner checks your teeth.

7. How many biting teeth have you got and how many chewing ones? Which teeth have the most fillings?

Tooth types

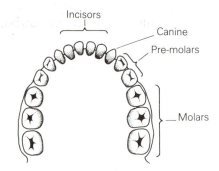

Figure 7.11 The different types of teeth

You have four different sorts of teeth (see Figure 7.11). Incisors and canines are biting teeth, and premolars and molars are chewing ones. You cannot really tell the difference between premolars and molars, but look in a mirror. Can you see the difference between incisors and canines?

7.6 Tooth structure

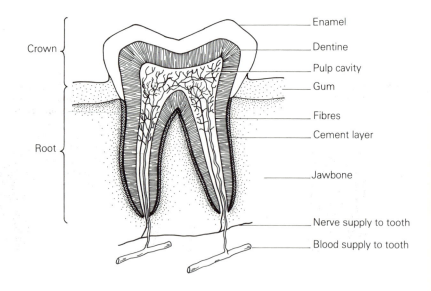

Figure 7.12 A molar tooth cut open

All you can see of your teeth is the white, hard tops. Most of the tooth is firmly held inside the jawbone, and, of course, if it were not it could easily fall out. The tooth in Figure 7.12 is a molar, but all the other teeth have the same structure—they are just a different shape. The white *enamel* is the hard biting surface, it is the hardest part of the body. *Dentine* is a little like bone and is what most of the tooth is made of. The tooth is alive so it needs blood, to carry food, and nerves. These nerves quickly tell us when something is wrong with the tooth. Finally the whole tooth is firmly held into your jawbone by *fibres* and *cement*. The fibres act like a shock absorber so that the vibrations from chewing do not pass into the bones of the head.

7.7 Tooth decay

Bacteria normally live in our mouths, and they feed on any traces of food which may be left stuck to our teeth. They turn the food into acid, and the mixture of bacteria and food and acid is called *plaque*. It forms all the time, and it is impossible to stop it. The acid, if left, dissolves the enamel and passes into the dentine which is softer. It dissolves the dentine more quickly than the enamel. This is called tooth *decay* or *caries*. Painful toothache occurs if the caries spreads to the nerves inside the tooth. (See Figure 7.13.)

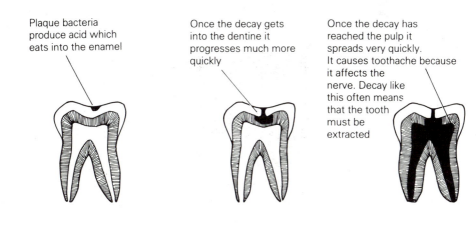

Plaque bacteria produce acid which eats into the enamel

Once the decay gets into the dentine it progresses much more quickly

Once the decay has reached the pulp it spreads very quickly. It causes toothache because it affects the nerve. Decay like this often means that the tooth must be extracted

Figure 7.13   Tooth decay

Preventing decay

To prevent caries we must make sure that the plaque is frequently cleaned off our teeth. This is done by careful brushing to scrape it off. Plaque collects in any tiny cracks and spaces, especially between the teeth and on the tops of the molars. To remove it you must brush with a good toothbrush, not an old one that you have had for years. Brush from the gums upwards (downwards on the top teeth) to sweep the plaque out (see Figure 7.14). Be careful to clean the backs of the teeth and also the number 7 and 8 teeth which are more awkward to get at.

Fluoride in the toothpaste or in the water we drink, helps to make the enamel stronger and more resistant to decay.

Brush the outside
of the teeth by
vibrating the brush
in a circular motion

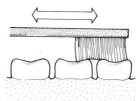

Brush the backs of
the teeth by sweeping
the brush away from
the gums

Brush the tops of
the teeth by a
backwards–forwards
movement

Figure 7.14 Tooth brushing

Brushing your teeth

1. Trace or draw two copies of the tooth plan for Experiment 7.5.

2. Take a disclosing tablet which stains bacteria red. Put the tablet in your mouth and let it dissolve. Swish this liquid all around your teeth, making sure they are all covered for a few seconds.

3. Spit the red liquid out into a sink and rinse it away.

4. Use a mirror to check which parts of your teeth and gums have been stained by the tablet. Get your partner to check your back teeth with a sterilised dental mirror. Mark carefully on the first tooth plan the stained areas.

5. Brush your teeth and rinse your mouth.

6. Take another disclosing tablet and stain your mouth as before.

7. Check for bacteria and mark any that are still visible on your second tooth plan.

8. Did you clean your teeth as well as possible? Which areas were easy to clean and which were most difficult?

7.8 Enzymes

Once the food is chewed into small pieces, it is then worked on by special chemicals in the digestive system. These are called *enzymes* and they break the food into smaller and smaller pieces and dissolve it. By breaking the food down they may change it from one substance to another. We have an enzyme in our mouth which does this (see Figure 7.15 over the page).

157

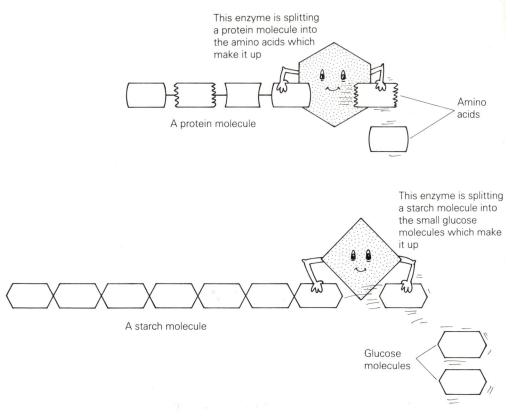

This enzyme is splitting a protein molecule into the amino acids which make it up

A protein molecule

Amino acids

This enzyme is splitting a starch molecule into the small glucose molecules which make it up

A starch molecule

Glucose molecules

Figure 7.15   How enzymes work

Experiment 7.7

The digestion of starch by saliva

HYPOTHESIS: that starch can be digested by a substance in saliva

1.   Take three clean test-tubes, labelled A, B, C, and a clean boiling tube. Stand them in a test-tube rack and get a spare test-tube and a white tile.

2.   Collect about 6 cm³ of saliva in the boiling tube. You may find it is easier to make saliva if you chew a clean rubber band.

3.   Treat the test-tubes in the following way:

Tube A.   Add about 3 cm³ of 1% starch solution and about 3 cm³ of distilled water.

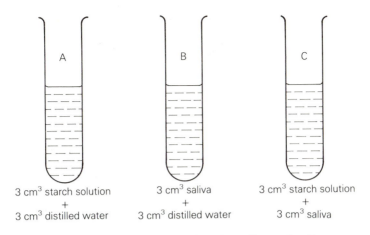

3 cm³ starch solution
+
3 cm³ distilled water

3 cm³ saliva
+
3 cm³ distilled water

3 cm³ starch solution
+
3 cm³ saliva

Figure 7.16   Apparatus for investigating the effect of saliva on starch

Tube B.   Add about 3 cm³ of saliva and about 3 cm³ of distilled water.

Tube C.   Add about 3 cm³ of 1% starch solution and 3 cm³ of saliva. (See Figure 7.16.)

4.   Take a drop of liquid from tube A with a glass rod. Put the drop on to the white tile. Clean the rod and take a drop from B and then from C. Test each drop with iodine. Record your results.

5.   Wait 10 minutes.

6.   Do step 4 again and record your results.

7.   Add about 2 cm³ of blue Benedict's solution to each tube and do the test for simple sugar.

8.   Record all your results in a chart like the one below:

Tube	*Starch present at start*	*Starch present at finish*	*Sugar present at finish*
A			
B			
C			

9.   In which tube did starch disappear? In which tube did sugar appear? Was the hypothesis correct?

7.9 The digestive system

There are several different enzymes in the digestive system which all work on different substances. For this reason the digestive system is divided up into a number of parts. You may remember some of the parts from the dissection of the rats.

The parts of the digestive system

1. Trace an outline of the body from pp. 56–57.

2. Figure 7.17 shows the parts of the digestive system. Trace around them on to some white paper.

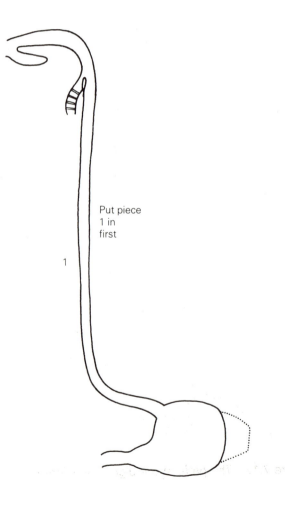

Put piece
1 in
first

1

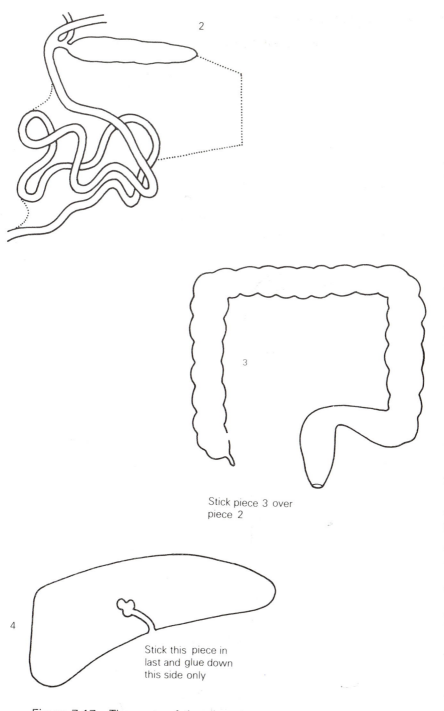

2

3

Stick piece 3 over
piece 2

4

Stick this piece in
last and glue down
this side only

Figure 7.17   The parts of the digestive system

3. Colour in the different parts and then cut them out.

4. You can now glue them on to your outline body. You can see from Figure 7.18 how they should go. Glue piece 1 first, followed by piece 2, then 3 and finally piece 4 which is glued down the left side only.

5. Label your diagram.

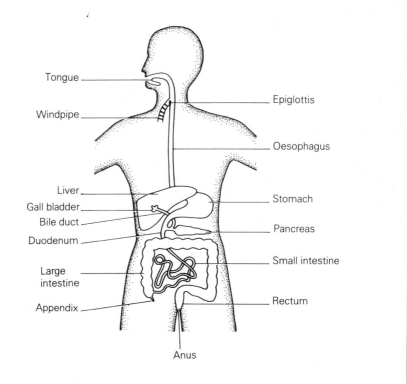

Figure 7.18   The complete digestive system

What happens in the digestive system is this:

(a) Food is chewed in the mouth into small pieces. Some starch is digested.

(b) It is swallowed down the *gullet*, or *oesophagus*, into the *stomach*. The gullet has muscles for swallowing and you can swallow even if you are standing on your head (try eating a piece of bread upside down).

(c) In the stomach, proteins are digested and many microbes are killed by the acid which the stomach walls produce. Food stays in the stomach for up to six hours and is continually mixed by the stomach squeezing until it is a semi-liquid mash.

(d) This leaves the stomach for the *duodenum*, where any starch left is digested. Fats and proteins are digested, too, and the enzymes for all this digestion are made in the *pancreas*. The *liver* helps to digest fats by producing *bile* which breaks fats down.

(e) In the *small intestine* all the digestion is completed by a number of enzymes. The digested substances are now in a form the body can use, so they pass through the small intestine wall and into the blood which carries them to all the parts of the body where they are needed. Getting food into the blood is a slow job and to get enough through, the small intestine has to be very long. In humans it is between 6 and 9 metres long, and because it has a special surface inside it is thought to have a total surface area of about 30 m^2.

(f) What passes into the *large intestine* is a very watery mash. It contains lots of water, which the large intestine takes back, and substances which cannot be digested, like plant fibres. These are stored for a while and then pass out through a small muscular hole called the *anus*.

The appendix

The appendix is a small tube attached to the large intestine. It has no job in Man and occasionally becomes full of digested food. If it becomes blocked, microbes which are always present in the digestive system can start an infection. In very extreme cases this gets out of control and the appendix starts to swell. Doctors have found that the simplest thing to do is to cut out the appendix before the infection spreads.

Making a model of the digestive system

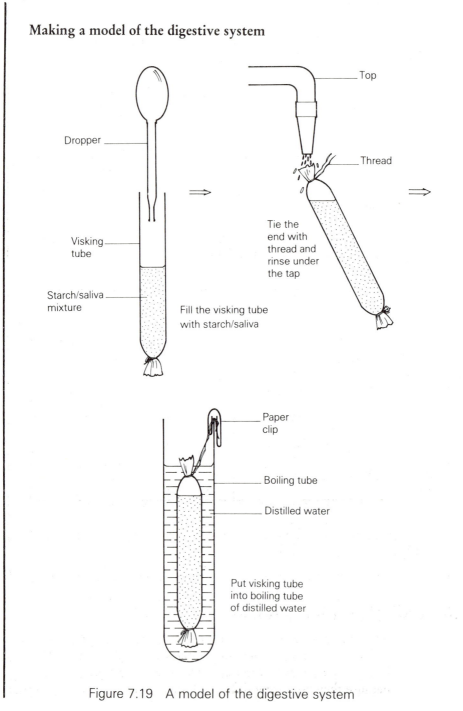

Figure 7.19   A model of the digestive system

1. Take a clean boiling tube and collect about 3 cm³ of saliva in it as in Experiment 7.7.

2. Add to this 6 – 8 cm³ of starch solution. This mixture will represent the food digesting in the model.

3. Take a second clean boiling tube and a piece of visking tube which is tied at one end. You also need a piece of cotton, a paper clip and a dropper.

4. Carefully half fill the visking tube with the starch/saliva mixture, and then tie the top of the visking tube with the thread. Now rinse the outside of the tube under a tap to make sure there is no starch/saliva on the outside.

5. Half fill the second boiling tube with distilled water and drop the visking tube in, as in the Figure 7.19.

6. Test the water in the boiling tube straight away for starch or simple sugar. Record your results in a table.

7. Wait 15 minutes, now test the water in the boiling tube again for starch and simple sugar.

	Starch	*Simple sugar*
Test on the water immediately after the visking tube was added		
Test on the water 15 minutes later		

8. Did starch pass through the visking tube? Did sugar pass through it? Where would the sugar have come from?

7.10 Feeding in other animals

All animals have the same problem of getting food into the body and then digesting it. Digestion is the same in all animals, that is, it is done by enzymes. Different animals feed in different ways, often because they are eating different foods. Here are a few examples:

The dog   Dogs eat mainly meat and bones. They have strong, sharp teeth used to tear meat apart and crunch bones. In particular, they have longer canine teeth (sometimes called *fangs*) which hook into the meat and are used for tearing it up. Pet dogs, of course, do not have to catch their own meat and do not need their canines so much.

The sheep   Grass, which sheep eat, has to be ground up to release the substances inside the cells. Sheep have rows of ridged molars and premolars which they grind round and round. If you watch a sheep or horse or cow, or other herbivore, you can see it chewing from side to side. Sheep have a row of sharp teeth at the front which chop the grass against a hard pad in the top jaw. In this way they can eat grass very close to the ground. Cows pull grass with their tongues and need to feed on fairly long grass.

The fly   Flies feed by sucking up liquids through a large pad. They land on food and produce saliva through their mouthparts, which dissolves the food. They then suck up the liquid. You can often see them doing this if they land on your arm. On you, they are feeding on the salt in your sweat.

The mosquito

Mosquitos suck blood using long, needle-like mouthparts which they stick into the skin. Just like the fly, they produce some saliva but this is to stop the blood from clotting. They then suck up the liquid blood.

The Amoeba

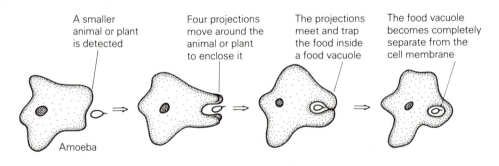

A smaller animal or plant is detected

Four projections move around the animal or plant to enclose it

The projections meet and trap the food inside a food vacuole

The food vacuole becomes completely separate from the cell membrane

Amoeba

Figure 7.20   An Amoeba feeding

Being only one-celled the Amoeba has to swallow its food whole. It feeds on smaller protozoans by completely enclosing them, as shown in Figure 7.20. Its cell membrane is able to join up with other parts so the food ends up inside the Amoeba in a drop of water. It is digested inside its tiny 'prison' called a *food vacuole*.

Experiment 7.9

Watching other animals feed

1. Select an animal in your home, garden or in a local park. It may be a dog or cat or you may choose a bird or insect. Try to choose an animal you do not know much about.

2. Watch it feeding. What is it feeding on? How exactly is it eating?

3. Try to describe how your animal feeds. It may help you to draw a labelled picture.

Questions on Chapter 7

1. List the three reasons why we must eat.

2. List the seven sorts of food types we need.

Fill in the blanks in the following sentences:

3. _____ and _____ are energy foods, whereas _____ are used to make the living material of cells. The mineral _____ is used in bones and teeth and _____ is needed to make blood. _____ is also needed for bones and teeth but in addition it is used inside cell nuclei. Vitamin _____ helps us to see in the dark and vitamin _____ makes bones grow strong. _____ was a disease caused by people not having enough vitamin C.

4. To test for simple sugar, warm a little food with _____ and if sugar is present it will change from _____ to _____/ _____._____ is the substance used to test for starch. A _____/ _____ colour shows starch is present. To test for protein you need _____ followed by _____ and a _____ colour will tell you that protein is present. There are

two tests for _____. One uses _____ and water, and the other is making a _____ spot on a piece of paper.

5. We have four sorts of teeth, _____ and _____ which are biting teeth, and _____ and _____ which are chewing teeth. The white part of the teeth is called the _____ and is the _____ part of the body. Most of a tooth is made of _____ and is buried in the jawbone.

6. Describe the steps you would take to avoid letting your teeth decay. Draw a diagram of a tooth showing how caries attacks teeth.

7. The _____ produces acid which kills some microbes. It also produces an enzyme which digests _____. The _____ produces enzymes which digest starch, proteins and _____ and the liver helps by producing _____. Digestion is completed in the _____ and the digested 'food' passes into the _____. Water is taken back from the liquid mash in the _____ and the undigestible remains are passed out through the _____.

8. Plan a menu for a day's meals, which provides a balanced intake of food types. Then list the food types showing which foods from your menu provide what food type.

9. Describe the differences between the teeth of a herbivore and a carnivore. Explain why they must have different tooth arrangements.

Crossword on Chapter 7

Across

1 and 4 down. The right foods for healthy living (8, 4)
6 A mineral used in blood cells (4)
7 Tooth decay (6)
9 We like a food's _____ to be pleasant (5)
10 A food containing 5 down (4)
13 18 down helps keep it in (4)
14 and 16 down. A pleasant cold food made from milk fat (3, 5)
15 A fruit to cure scurvy (4)
17 Calcium helps make bones _____ (4)
19 Another fruit to cure scurvy (5)
20 A food—50% of it is 18 down (6)
21 A chemical helping to break down food (6)

Down

2 A fruit that is good for your 11 down! (5)
3 A food type—there's a lot of it in rice (12)
4 See 1 across
5 A food type—it's used to make cells (7)
8 A mineral to make nerves work properly (4)
10 A good source of minerals usually left on the doorstep (4)
11 They collect plaque (5)
12 Most of what 11 down are made of (7)
16 See 14 across
18 A food type—a white, greasy substance (3)

Trace this grid on to a piece of paper, and then fill in the answers.

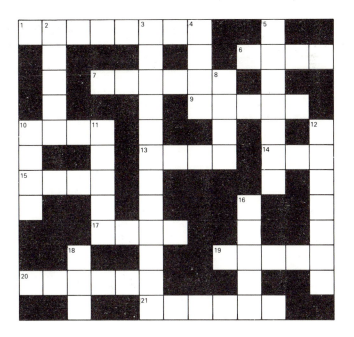

8. How plants feed

8.1 Early experiments

For many centuries scientists assumed that plants got all the food they needed from the soil by taking it in through their roots. An experiment done by a scientist called Jean-Baptiste van Helmont (1577–1644) was published in 1668 (long after his death). Van Helmont had put 200 lb (about 91 kg) of dry soil in an iron pot and covered it with a lid with holes in. He planted, through a large central hole in the lid, a young willow tree weighing 5 lb (2.25 kg). The pot and tree were left in his garden for five years, and watered when necessary with distilled water if no rain had fallen. Each autumn the tree shed its leaves which were swept away.

After five years the tree was dug up and weighed and found to weigh 169 lb 3 oz (about 77 kg). The soil was carefully collected and dried and weighed. It came to only 2 oz (about 30 g) less than 200 lb. Van Helmont concluded that the plant had grown from water alone. (See Figure 8.1.)

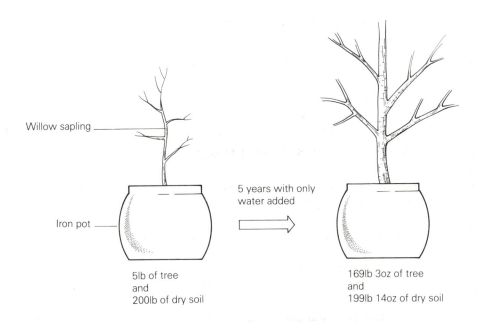

Willow sapling

Iron pot

5 years with only water added

5lb of tree
and
200lb of dry soil

169lb 3oz of tree
and
199lb 14oz of dry soil

Figure 8.1   van Helmont's experiment

Joseph Priestley (1733–1804) also experimented with plants. He put a few shoots of mint into a sealed bell jar and then burned a candle in the jar until it went out, having used up all the oxygen. He left the jar for a few days and then found that he could light the candle and it would burn again. He could not do this if the bell jar had no mint in it. He concluded that the mint had 'restored' the air, and what he meant was that the mint had replaced the oxygen that the candle had used. (See Figure 8.2.)

You too can do this experiment.

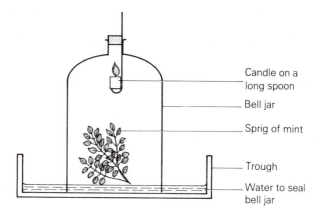

Figure 8.2   Priestley's experiment

Demonstration Experiment 8.1

Priestley's experiment

HYPOTHESIS: that plants produce oxygen

1. Take a large bell jar and a glass trough.

2. Stand a small potted plant, or a few shoots of privet in a beaker of water, in the trough.

3. Pour in a centimetre of water and stand the bell jar in the trough.

4. Assemble a candle on a long deflagrating spoon with a bung. Check that the candle does not touch the plant when it is in place.

5. Light the candle and put it into the bell jar, sealing it in with the bung (see Figure 8.3 over the page). Time how long it takes to go out.

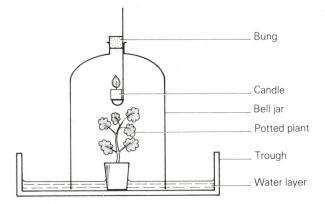

Bung

Candle

Bell jar

Potted plant

Trough

Water layer

Figure 8.3 A repeat of Priestley's experiment

6. Leave the apparatus, untouched, in a light place for two or three days.

7. Quickly remove the bung and candle and re-stopper the bell jar with a spare bung.

8. Re-light the candle and replace it in the jar. Time how long it takes to go out.

9. Was the hypothesis correct?

From these two early experiments it was shown that plants take very little, except water, from the soil, and that they do change the air. It seemed, therefore, that plants somehow feed on air (or something in it) and water.

8.2 Plants and light

It quickly became clear that light was also important, since Priestley's experiment would not work if the bell jar was left in a dark corner of his lab. The three ingredients necessary for plants to grow well are, therefore, *light*, *water* and *air*. The part of air which is important is carbon dioxide which can be shown in the following experiment.

172

Experiment 8.2

The reactions of plants and carbon dioxide gas

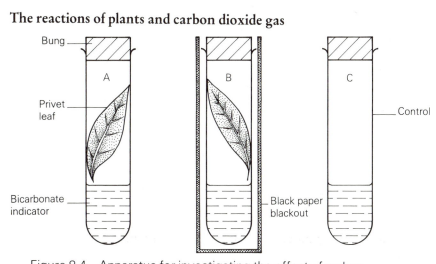

Figure 8.4   Apparatus for investigating the effect of carbon dioxide on a plant

1. Take three test-tubes marked A, B, C.

2. To each tube add about 2 cm depth of bicarbonate indicator. (This detects the presence of carbon dioxide by turning yellow. It goes purplish when all traces of carbon dioxide are removed.) Do not breath on the tubes.

3. Wedge a single large privet leaf into tubes A and B and put bungs into all the tubes. Tube C is a control.

4. Wrap black paper around tube B so that no light can get in.

5. Leave in a well-lit place, e.g. by a window, for four to six hours.

6. Check the colour of the indicator in each tube. Record your results in a table:

Tube	Colour at start	Colour at end	Explanation
A			
B			
C			

8.3 Photosynthesis

The reaction between plants, light, water and carbon dioxide is called *photosynthesis*. This is the way in which plants make their food. Light is a form of energy which green plants can absorb. It is used to join water and carbon dioxide together to make the sugar glucose, which is quickly turned into starch. In this reaction oxygen gas is produced as a waste product and is released by the plant (as Priestley discovered). The reaction is summarised by this equation:

$$\text{Carbon dioxide} + \text{Water} \xrightarrow{\text{Light}} \text{Glucose} + \text{Oxygen}$$

Using chemical symbols the reaction is:

$$6CO_2 + 6H_2O \xrightarrow{\text{Light}} C_6H_{12}O_6 + 6O_2 \uparrow$$

A summary of photosynthesis is shown in Figure 8.5.

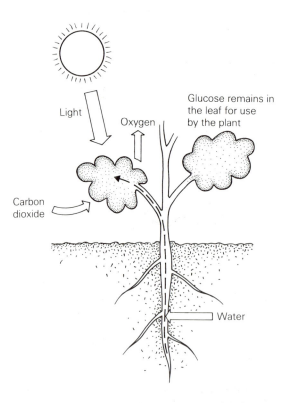

Figure 8.5   A summary of photosynthesis

The glucose, as well as being turned into starch, can be turned into proteins using minerals from the soil, which explains why van Helmont's soil lost 2 oz.

The parts of the plant which do photosynthesis are the *chloroplasts*. These are tiny green discs found inside the plant cells and which give green plants their colour. Chloroplasts contain the substance *chlorophyll*. Plants like mushrooms, which are not green, cannot photosynthesise.

There are a number of experiments which show that photosynthesis has taken place. They all rely on being able to detect starch in the leaves. The experiment to do this is shown below.

Experiment 8.3

Starch testing on leaves

1. Cut a small piece of a geranium leaf using scissors or a cork borer (see Figure 8.6).

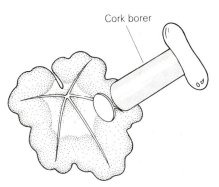

Cork borer

Figure 8.6   Cutting a leaf with a cork borer

2. Put the piece of leaf into boiling water for about a minute, to soften it (see Figure 8.7 over the page).

3. Put about 10 cm³ of ethanol in a boiling tube along with the leaf. *Remove the Bunsen* from under the beaker, because ethanol, liquid or vapour, catches fire very easily and must *never* be put near a naked flame. Stand the boiling tube in the beaker and the ethanol will begin to boil (see Figure 8.8 over the page).

175

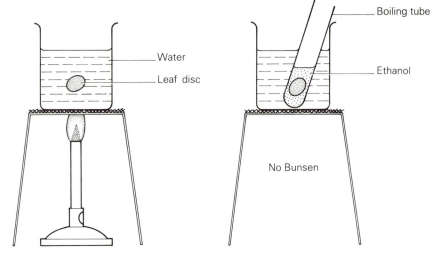

Figure 8.7   Softening a leaf   Figure 8.8   *Don't* heat ethanol!

4. Allow the ethanol to boil until the leaf has turned white. If the ethanol stops boiling then heat the water again but take the boiling tube out of the beaker first.

5. Remove the white piece of leaf from the ethanol and put it back into the hot water for about a minute.

6. Put the leaf on to a white tile and add one or two drops of iodine (see Figure 8.9). Wait a few minutes for a blue/black colour to appear showing starch is present.

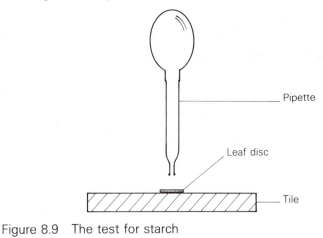

Figure 8.9   The test for starch

Investigating photosynthesis and light

HYPOTHESIS: that light is necessary for photosynthesis

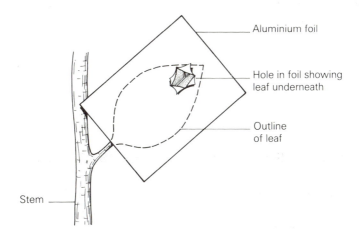

Aluminium foil

Hole in foil showing
leaf underneath

Outline
of leaf

Stem

Figure 8.10   A leaf partly kept in the dark

1. Take a piece of aluminium foil large enough to completely cover a leaf both sides.

2. Cut out a small hole in the foil.

3. Fold the foil around a leaf of a potted plant so that the hole is over the top of the leaf near one edge. The rest of the leaf must be completely covered by the foil (see Figure 8.10).

4. Leave this for three or four days.

5. Remove the foil and cut out a piece of leaf so that it has a part which was covered by foil and part which was under the hole.

6. Test this piece for starch.

7. Was starch present over the whole piece, only in the part that was covered by foil, or only in the part that was not covered?

Investigating photosynthesis and chlorophyll

HYPOTHESIS: that chlorophyll is necessary for photosynthesis

1. Take a small piece of leaf from a variegated plant (one which has green and white leaves) such as a tradescantia or variegated geranium. Make sure your leaf has both green and white parts.

2. Do the starch test on this.

3. Was starch present all over the leaf, only in the white parts or only in the green parts?

8.4 How fast does photosynthesis happen?

If you look inside an aquarium on a sunny day, you will see bubbles around the leaves of the plants. These bubbles are oxygen which the plant is producing. It is possible to count these bubbles to see how quickly photosynthesis is taking place.

Experiment 8.6

Measuring the rate of photosynthesis

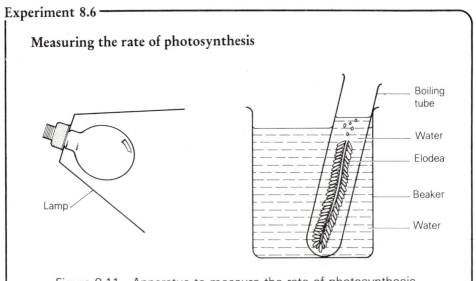

Figure 8.11   Apparatus to measure the rate of photosynthesis

1. Take a fresh shoot of Canadian pond weed (Elodea).

2. Put it upside down in a boiling tube of fresh water. Put this into a beaker of water which will help keep the temperature constant.

3. Put a bench lamp 10 cm away from the beaker and switch the lamp on. Draw all the blinds so that the room is dark.

4. Wait three or four minutes for the plant to stabilise.

5. Count the number of bubbles which rise from the stem in five minutes. Record the results in a table.

6. Move the lamp to 20 cm from the beaker and wait three or four minutes, and then count the bubbles again for five minutes.

7. Repeat with the lamp at 30 and 40 cm.

Distance/cm	Number of bubbles
10	
20	
30	
40	

8. When was photosynthesis quickest?

8.5 Leaf structure

Leaves are the parts of the plant where most photosynthesis takes place. They are adapted specially to be able to photosynthesise efficiently. They always face the light, and they are thin and flat to catch as much light as possible. They are arranged on a stem so that they shade other leaves as little as possible.

If you look inside a leaf you will see that it is arranged for photosynthesis. Most of the chlorophyll is near the upper side, which is why leaves are darker on top than underneath. It also has tiny holes in to let carbon dioxide in and oxygen out of the leaf. These holes are almost always found on the underside of the leaf and they can be quite easily seen with a microscope. They are called *stomata* (a single hole is called a *stoma*). The holes, themselves, are shaped like a rugby ball and have two banana-shaped cells, called *guard cells*, around them. (See Figure 8.12 over the page.)

179

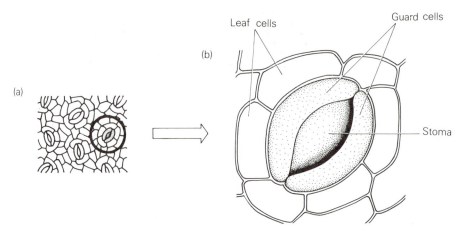

Figure 8.12   (a) Several stomata as they appear on a leaf, (b) a single stoma very highly magnified

To see them you cannot just put a leaf on a microscope. It is too thick and will not let enough light through. It is easier to take an imprint of the underside of the leaf.

Experiment 8.7

Looking at stomata

1. Paint the underside of a privet leaf with a thin layer of nail varnish. Leave it to dry.

2. Set up a microscope with the low-power objective.

3. Using forceps, peel off the dry nail varnish and lay it on a glass slide in a drop of water.

4. Examine the nail varnish for stomata. They are very small.

5. Make a simple diagram of two or three stomata.

Stomata are not simply holes; they can be closed by the guard cells, and this happens every night (see Figure 8.13). This is because plants lose water through the stomata and they cut down water loss by closing them when photosynthesis is not taking place.

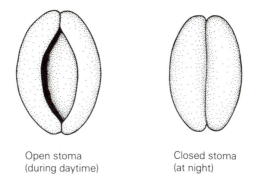

Open stoma   Closed stoma
(during daytime)   (at night)

Figure 8.13   The effect of light on a single stoma

Leaf cells   A cross-section of a leaf shows an arrangement of cells as in Figure 8.14. A cross-section is where a cut has been made across the leaf from top to bottom and a thin slice, or section, removed. This can be examined with a microscope.

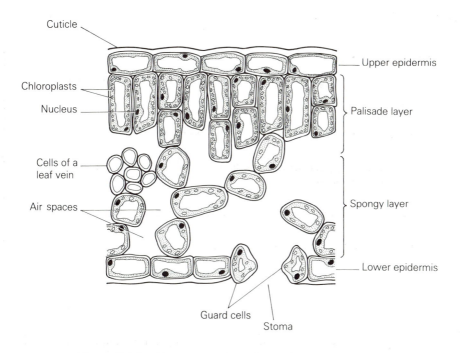

Figure 8.14   A cross-section of a leaf

181

Looking at cross-sections of leaves

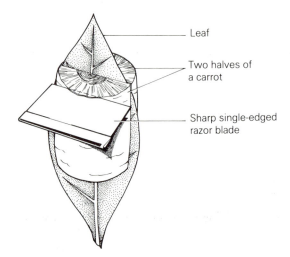

Figure 8.15   Preparing a cross-section of a leaf

1. Set up a microscope for low-power viewing.

2. Take a fresh leaf from any suitable plant and hold it between two halves of a piece of carrot as in Figure 8.15.

3. Carefully, using a very sharp razor blade and cutting away from you, cut as thin a slice of carrot as you can. By cutting the carrot you will also cut a cross-section of the leaf, but to be of any use the section must be so thin that you can only just see it.

4. Put a number of sections on a clean slide in a drop of water. Cover with a cover slip.

5. Examine the sections and try to find a good cross-section. Make a clear labelled sketch of it. How does it compare with the diagram in the book?

6. Repeat this with other sorts of leaves.

7. If you cannot cut good sections then examine prepared slides of leaves instead. Remember to draw clear, labelled diagrams.

The leaf has a *cuticle* on top which is waterproof and stops water from escaping. Under this is the *upper epidermis*, made of thin, flat cells which do not have chlorophyll. Then there is the *palisade mesophyll* layer, the cells which do most of the photosynthesis. They are tall, thin cells which have lots of chloroplasts. Below these are the cells of the *spongy mesophyll* layer. It is called this because of all the air spaces between the cells. It is here that carbon dioxide is taken in and oxygen released from the cells. The leaf *veins*, bringing water and taking away the substances made during photosynthesis, also pass through the spongy mesophyll. The lower side of the leaf is called the *lower epidermis* which also has a cuticle and the stomata with their guard cells.

8.6 The importance of photosynthesis

Food chains Besides being important to plants, photosynthesis is a vital process to all animals. Animals eat plants or they eat other animals which have fed on plants. If plants were not able to grow quickly by photosynthesising quickly, then there would soon be no food left for animals to eat. This arrangement where one organism feeds on another is called a *food chain*.

Figure 8.16   A food chain

In Figure 8.16 you can trace the energy which starts out as light from the Sun. This is trapped by the grass which is then eaten by the cow. The cow digests the grass and uses some of its energy to grow. Man then eats the cow in the form of beef and gets some of his energy from it. A food chain like this is often drawn in this form:

$$Grass \longrightarrow Cow \longrightarrow Man$$

Food webs Of course we do not just eat beef. We also eat pork, chicken and fish, as well as getting a lot of energy by eating plants directly (for example, wheat and rice). To represent this complicated feeding system we can use what is called a *food web*. Part of a food web is shown in Figure 8.17.

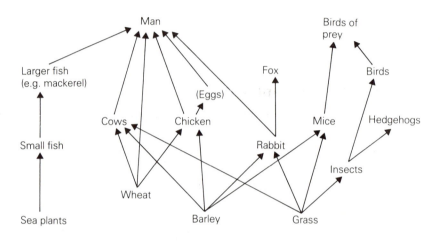

Figure 8.17 A simplified food web

No matter how complicated the web gets, the bottom line is always plants and the energy for all this life comes from the Sun.

Oxygen As well as providing us with food, plants also provide our oxygen. Every animal uses oxygen and produces carbon dioxide during respiration. The oxygen has to be replaced if the world is not to run out of it. Nature has arranged that plants, by their normal living, use up the carbon dioxide and produce oxygen. This cycle is just one of the many cycles which Nature uses to keep important substances going round so that they are never used up. (See Figure 8.18.)

Much of the oxygen comes from tiny single-celled plants in the sea which are part of the plankton. Lots, too, come from the vast tropical forests of Africa and South America.

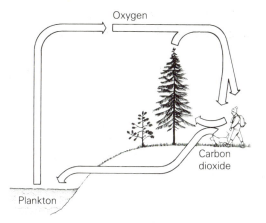

Figure 8.18   The oxygen/carbon dioxide cycle

Questions on Chapter 8

1. What did van Helmont and Priestley prove by their experiments?

2. In the experiment using the apparatus of Figure 8.19 what would be the colour of the bicarbonate indicator in each of the tubes A, B and C, after six hours of daylight?

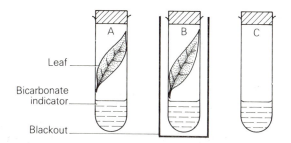

Figure 8.19   See Question 2

3. Fill in the blanks in the reaction for photosynthesis:

   Carbon dioxide + _____ ⟶ Glucose + _____
   _____ + __H_2O ⟶ $C_6H_{12}O_6$ + _____

4. Fill in the blanks:
   To test a leaf for the presence of starch first cut out a disc of leaf and _____ it in _____ for about a minute. Then remove the _____ _____ from under the water and put a boiling

185

tube of _____ into the beaker. Add the leaf disc to this and _____ until the leaf goes _____. Remove the leaf and replace it into the _____ for about a minute. Remove the leaf and put it on to a _____ _____. Add a few drops _____ solution and a _____ _____ colour shows starch is present.

5. Draw a clear labelled diagram of a cross-section of a leaf. Explain in your own words why a leaf is an efficient organ for photosynthesis.

6. Write down five simple food chains, each with at least three organisms in.

7. Write down one food chain with four organisms in it.

8. From your own knowledge, make up a food web.

Wordfinder on Chapter 8

Trace the wordfinder on to a piece of paper. Then solve the following clues and put a ring around the answers. Answers go in any direction: across, back, up, down and diagonally. The answer to Question 1 is ringed already to give you a start.

1　He did an experiment with a candle in a bell jar (7) . . .
2　. . . What else did he put in the bell jar? (4)
3　He did an experiment with a tree (3, 7)
4　. . . What sort of a tree? (6)
5　A tree is a large _____ (5)
6　One thing plants must have (5)
7　Another thing plants must have (5)
8　Yet another thing plants must have (3)
9　The gas plants produce (6)
10　People once thought plants got all their food from the _____ (4) . . .
11　. . . and this food would come up through their _____ (5)
12　Now we know they get it from a reaction called _____ (14)
13　A tiny green disc inside a plant cell (11) . . .
14　. . . A substance inside this green disc (11)
15　Carbon dioxide turns bicarbonate indicator this colour (6)
16　Light helps carbon dioxide and water to produce *this* (7) . . .
17　. . . which is soon turned into *this* (6)
18　The Canadian pond weed (6)

19 It always faces the light (4) ...
20 and it has small holes on its underside called _____ (7) ...
21 ... These holes each have two _____ _____ around them (5, 5)
22 A 19 has a _____ on top which is waterproof (7) ...
23 ... Under this is something made of thin flat cells—called the _____ _____ (5, 9)
24 The cells which do most of the 12 are in the _____ mesophyll layer (8) ...
25 ... Below this is the _____ mesophyll layer (6)
26 A _____ brings water and takes away substances made during 12 (4)
27 Grass — Cow — Man is a _____ chain (4) ...
28 ... A more complicated system is shown in a 27 _____ (3)

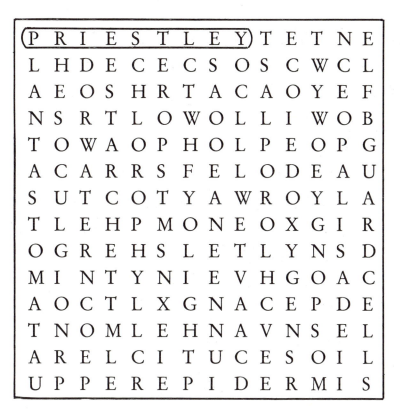

P	R	I	E	S	T	L	E	Y	T	E	T	N	E
L	H	D	E	C	E	C	S	O	S	C	W	C	L
A	E	O	S	H	R	T	A	C	A	O	Y	E	F
N	S	R	T	L	O	W	O	L	L	I	W	O	B
T	O	W	A	O	P	H	O	L	P	E	O	P	G
A	C	A	R	R	S	F	E	L	O	D	E	A	U
S	U	T	C	O	T	Y	A	W	R	O	Y	L	A
T	L	E	H	P	M	O	N	E	O	X	G	I	R
O	G	R	E	H	S	L	E	T	L	Y	N	S	D
M	I	N	T	Y	N	I	E	V	H	G	O	A	C
A	O	C	T	L	X	G	N	A	C	E	P	D	E
T	N	O	M	L	E	H	N	A	V	N	S	E	L
A	R	E	L	C	I	T	U	C	E	S	O	I	L
U	P	P	E	R	E	P	I	D	E	R	M	I	S

9. The importance of water

9.1 Water

As we have already noticed, water is a simple substance which makes up nearly three-quarters of our bodies. If all this water were taken away, we would end up a few dry bones and a small pile of chemical dust! Plant seeds do not contain much water, as you have seen in Chapter 5, but the plants themselves may be little more than water. Lettuce, for example, is more than 90% water.

Since water makes up such a large percentage of living organisms, it must have a very important job inside them, but what exactly does it do? It does a number of different things, and does not do the same thing in plants and animals. If we think about animals first, then its main job is to dissolve substances. When a chemical dissolves in water, it forms a solution. Substances in solution can be easily transported around the body—for instance, food and oxygen is carried in our blood. Substances in solution can react with each other too. Chemical reactions which take place in our bodies, like digestion and tasting, cannot work if the substances are dry, so our food has to be well mixed with water as soon as it is put into our mouths. The next experiment shows this.

Experiment 9.1

Investigating whether water is necessary for taste

1. Make sure your hands are clean.

2. You will need a stop-clock, some sugar, some sugar solution and a drinking straw.

3. Place a pinch of sugar on your tongue (Figure 9.1), and at the same time start the stop-clock. Keep your mouth open, and do not let your tongue touch the roof or sides of your mouth.

4. Time how long it takes for you to be able to taste the sugar.

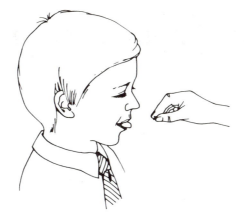

Figure 9.1   The start of the sugar experiment. Place a piece of
sugar on your tongue

5. Rinse out your mouth, and dry your tongue as completely as you can
    with clean blotting paper or paper towel.

6. Place a pinch of sugar on your dry tongue, and time how long it takes
    until you can taste it as before.

7. Rinse out your mouth again, and place a drop of sugar solution on
    your tongue using a straw. Once again time how long it takes to be
    able to taste it.

8. Record your results in a table. Which sugar could you taste quickest
    and which took the longest to taste?

9.2 Diffusion

Water allows reactions like taste and digestion to happen because it
allows *diffusion*. Only liquids and gases can diffuse because diffusion is the movement of the molecules of a substance. All substances are made of tiny particles, which you can never see called
molecules. In a solid, all the molecules are fixed together but in a
liquid or a gas they are not held so tightly and can move away from
each other.

Molecules may move away from or towards each other. You cannot see molecules moving but you can see diffusion.

189

Experiment 9.2

Demonstrating diffusion

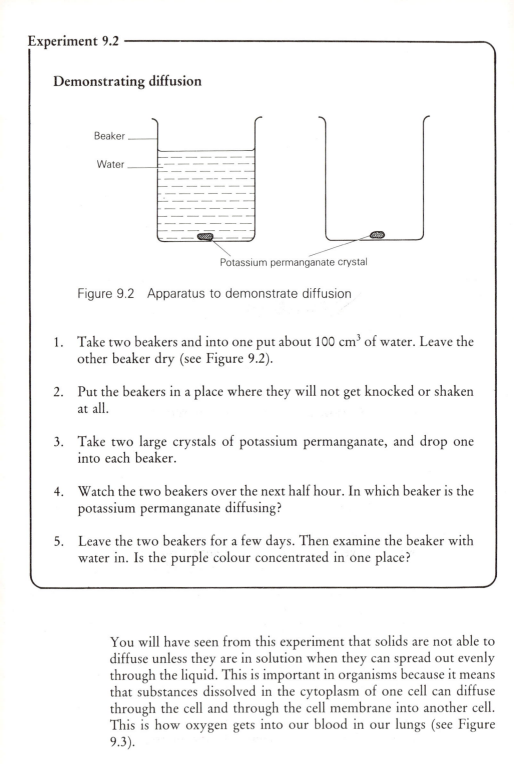

Figure 9.2   Apparatus to demonstrate diffusion

1. Take two beakers and into one put about 100 cm³ of water. Leave the other beaker dry (see Figure 9.2).

2. Put the beakers in a place where they will not get knocked or shaken at all.

3. Take two large crystals of potassium permanganate, and drop one into each beaker.

4. Watch the two beakers over the next half hour. In which beaker is the potassium permanganate diffusing?

5. Leave the two beakers for a few days. Then examine the beaker with water in. Is the purple colour concentrated in one place?

You will have seen from this experiment that solids are not able to diffuse unless they are in solution when they can spread out evenly through the liquid. This is important in organisms because it means that substances dissolved in the cytoplasm of one cell can diffuse through the cell and through the cell membrane into another cell. This is how oxygen gets into our blood in our lungs (see Figure 9.3).

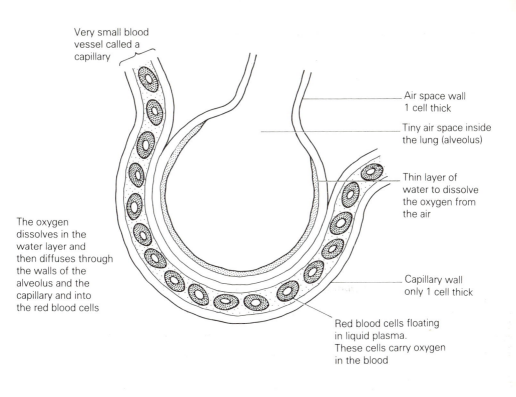

Very small blood vessel called a capillary

Air space wall 1 cell thick

Tiny air space inside the lung (alveolus)

Thin layer of water to dissolve the oxygen from the air

The oxygen dissolves in the water layer and then diffuses through the walls of the alveolus and the capillary and into the red blood cells

Capillary wall only 1 cell thick

Red blood cells floating in liquid plasma. These cells carry oxygen in the blood

Figure 9.3   How oxygen gets into the blood

9.3 Osmosis

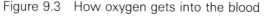

Since water is a liquid, it is also able to diffuse, and the diffusion of water is given the special name *osmosis*. Osmosis is one of the most important processes which take place inside living organisms.

Just as diffusion spreads substances out evenly, so osmosis spreads out water molecules evenly. The idea of water molecules being spread unevenly is hard to imagine but can be explained simply as follows.

Imagine a beaker with 100 cm³ of distilled water; the water is pure and contains only water molecules. Another beaker contains 100 cm³ of a 50% sugar solution. This is a strong solution, and because of the sugar the water molecules are more spread out than in distilled water. (See Figure 9.4 over the page.)

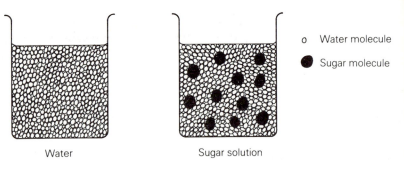

Water   Sugar solution

o   Water molecule

●   Sugar molecule

Figure 9.4   The beaker of water has more water molecules than the beaker of sugar solution

If these two liquids were mixed, we would not see diffusion like the potassium permanganate experiment because the solutions would just mix and the sugar and water would become evenly spread through the mixture. If, however, we could join the two liquids through a wall which only let water molecules through, then we would see the diffusion of water (see Figure 9.5).

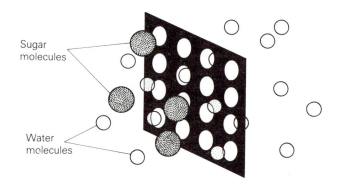

Sugar molecules

Water molecules

Figure 9.5   A semi-permeable membrane with holes in it which only let water molecules through

Water molecules are much smaller than sugar molecules and a wall with holes in it small enough to let water through and not sugar is called a *semi-permeable membrane*.

Obviously the holes are much too small for us to be able to see them. The water diffuses through the holes to try to spread out as evenly as possible. This means that water diffuses from the distilled water into the strong sugar solution. In general, water diffuses from a weak solution (distilled water is the weakest solution possible) to a strong solution.

Osmosis is, therefore, the diffusion of water from a weak solution to a strong one through a semi-permeable membrane. The reason why osmosis is so important is that all cell membranes are semi-permeable membranes.

Demonstration Experiment 9.3

To show osmosis

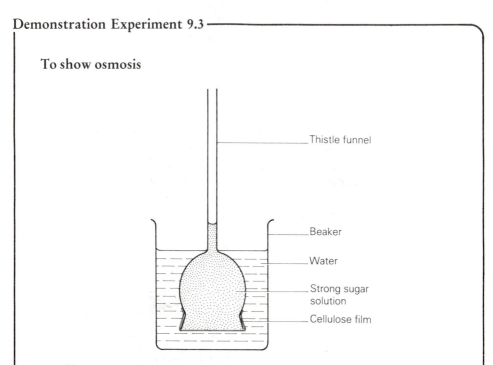

Figure 9.6   Apparatus to demonstrate osmosis

1. Hold a thistle funnel upside down and, with a finger over the tube, fill it almost completely with strong sugar solution.

2. Fix a sheet of cellulose film over the wide end of the funnel using an elastic band.

3. Turn the funnel the right way up and check for leaks.

4. Lower the funnel into a beaker of water and mark on the stem of the funnel the level of the sugar solution.

5. Leave for 20 minutes, then check the level of solution in the thistle funnel. Has the liquid level risen? Explain why.

Experiment 9.4

To show osmosis

1. Place five sultanas in a clean container of water. Leave for 24 hours.

2. What has happened to the sultanas? Eat one and compare it with one which has not been in water.

3. Explain as fully as you can, what has occurred.

Experiment 9.5

The effects of osmosis on blood cells

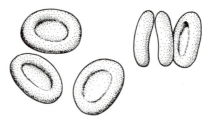

Figure 9.7 Red blood cells in their normal state in the blood. They appear a little like a doughnut because they are much thinner in the middle than around the edges. They are extremely small. There are about 5½ million in every cubic millimetre of blood

1. Set up a microscope for viewing under low power.

2. Take three glass slides marked A, B, and C and three cover slips.

3. On to each slide put a small drop of blood followed by:

   Slide A—a drop of distilled water.

   Slide B—a drop of 0.6% salt solution.

   Slide C—a drop of concentrated salt solution.

4. Cover each slide with a cover slip and then observe them under the microscope, starting with slide B. Observe first with low power, and then with high power if necessary. Figure 9.7 will remind you of what red blood cells look like.

5. Make clear sketches of two or three cells from each slide. Explain the difference between the cells on each slide.

9.4 Osmosis and animal cells

The movement of water in and out of cells may make a cell get bigger or smaller. Obviously this could seriously upset the way the cells work and hold together. Animals, like humans, try to allow as little osmosis as possible by keeping the solutions in the body all at the same concentration. The next experiment shows what could happen if this were not so.

Water control

Humans, like many other animals, lose water by breathing and sweating and replace it by drinking. This could lead to weak body solutions soon after a drink, gradually getting stronger with time, which would affect the normal working of cells. To control this we have *kidneys*. These take water out of the blood if there is too much in the body, but do not take any if the body water falls. The kidneys are controlled by the brain which checks the blood all the time. The kidneys also remove waste and poisonous substances from the blood. The liquid they produce is called *urine* and is passed to the *bladder* for storage, until it can be passed out of the body. On warm days, when we sweat a lot, we do not pass much urine. On cold days we pass much more.

Water animals

Of course, the animals with the biggest problems caused by osmosis are the ones which live in water. Fresh water, like that in rivers and ponds, is a weak solution which is always weaker than the solution inside animals. This means that water will always enter them by osmosis. To deal with this all freshwater animals have efficient ways of passing the water back out again. Fish have good kidneys. Some animals, too, are able to stop some water from coming in by having a fairly waterproof coat. Again some fish do this by covering themselves with slime.

Sea water, on the other hand, is a strong solution and is usually stronger than the solution inside animals. This means that sea animals are likely to lose water by osmosis and could actually dry out. To control this sea animals often have to drink lots of water and get rid of the salt from it. Many sea animals have a stronger solution than normal in their bodies.

For this reason people should not drink sea water. Instead of quenching our thirst it actually dries out our body from the inside.

195

9.5 Osmosis and plant cells

Plants need water to keep substances dissolved and also for photo-synthesis, and many plants need it to keep them upright. A plant which loses too much water wilts and becomes flabby.

The reason for this is that plant cells are blown up with water rather like a football is blown up with air. Plant cells have a vacuole which contains a fairly strong solution (see Chapter 3). Water around the cell passes into the vacuole by osmosis, making it swell up. This makes the whole cell swell until it is full. The cell wall is strong and will not burst and so the whole cell becomes hard and rigid. A cell like this is called *turgid*, and a stem or leaf made of turgid cells is able to be stiff and stand up (see Figure 9.8).

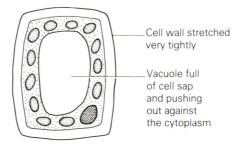

Figure 9.8   A turgid leaf cell

A plant cell which loses water gradually becomes flabby as the vacuole shrinks, until it gets so small that the cell cytoplasm is pulled away from the cell wall. If this happens the cell has no strength at all and is called *plasmolysed*. (See Figure 9.9.)

You can see turgid and plasmolysed cells in the next experiment.

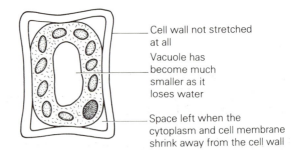

Figure 9.9   A plasmolysed leaf cell

The effects of osmosis on onion cells

1. Set up a microscope for viewing under low power.

2. Go back to Experiment 3.1 and follow instructions 2, 3 and 4 to remove two outside layers of onion.

3. Put one layer on a slide with distilled water and the other on a slide with strong sugar solution (see Figure 9.10). Make sure the onion layer is flat on the slide. Use a coverslip if necessary.

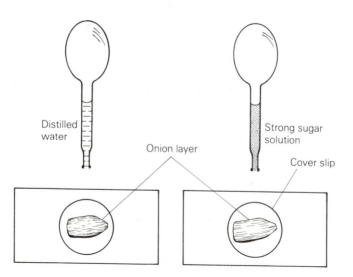

Figure 9.10 How to investigate osmosis in onion cells

4. Examine both slides carefully because the differences are not easy to see. Check with Figures 9.8 and 9.9 to see what a turgid and plasmolysed cell should look like.

5. Draw clear, labelled diagrams of two or three cells from each slide.

9.6 Getting water into a plant root

The way plant roots get water from soil also relies on osmosis. Soil contains water in the tiny space between soil particles. This water contains some dissolved substances, and so is a weak solution, much weaker than the solution inside the plant cells. Special cells called *root hair cells* stick out from the sides of the roots in between the soil particles. Water passes by osmosis from the soil into the vacuoles of the root hair cells (see Figure 9.11).

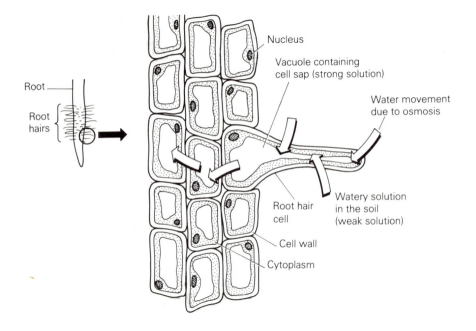

Figure 9.11   A root hair cell

This water makes the vacuoles of the root hair cells a weaker solution than the other cells around them. Once more, by osmosis, water passes from the root hair cells to other plant cells and in this way spreads through the root until it gets to special tubes which can carry water more quickly up the stem to other parts of the plant.

Looking at root hair cells

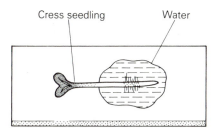

Figure 9.12   Preparing a cress seedling for a hand lens

1. Set up a microscope for viewing under low power.

2. Take a fresh cress seedling with its root and lay it on a slide so that the root is well covered with water (see Figure 9.12).

3. Examine the root using a hand lens to see the tiny root hair cells.

4. Now examine the root with the microscope, being careful not to spill water on the microscope.

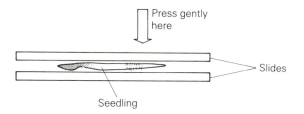

Figure 9.13   Preparing a cress seedling for a microscope

5. If root hair cells are not easy to see, then lay another slide over the root and gently squash it by pressing on the slide, as in Figure 9.13. This should spread the root cells out.

6. Examine the root again for root hair cells.

7. Make a clear labelled diagram of one root hair cell.

Questions on Chapter 9

Fill in the blanks in the following sentences.

1. Substances _____ in water to form a solution. Substances in solution can be _____ and can _____ with each other. Reactions in the body like _____ and _____ only work on solutions.

2. Diffusion is the _____ of _____ of _____ or _____, either towards or away from each other.

3. Osmosis is the diffusion of _____ from a _____ solution to a _____ one, through a _____ _____ membrane.

4. Explain carefully how osmosis happens. Why is osmosis important to living organisms?

5. In what three ways is water important to plants.

6. Fill in the blanks:

    A plant cell is turgid when its _____ is as full of _____ as it can be and the _____ is stretched tight. Turgid cells are _____. As _____ passes out of a vacuole the cell becomes _____ until the _____ gets so small that it pulls away from the cell wall. When this happens the cell is called _____.

7. Explain carefully the job of root hair cell.

Wordfinder on Chapter 9

Trace the wordfinder on to a piece of paper. Then solve the following clues and put a ring around the answers. Answers go in any direction: across, back, up, down and diagonally. The answer to Question 1 is ringed already to give you a start.

1 A simple substance which makes up nearly three-quarters of our bodies (5)
2 Substances in solution can be carried around the _____ (4)
3 It must be mixed with water to have a taste (4)
4 A liquid can _____ (7) . . .
5 . . . and so can a _____ (3) . . .

6 ... because their _____, which are tiny particles, can move (9)
7 The diffusion of water is called _____ (7)
8, 9. A 'wall' with holes in it small enough to let water through but not sugar is called a _____ _____ (13, 8: 2 words in separate places)
10 Sugar in water forms a _____ (8)
11 It removes waste from the blood (6) ...
12 ... and produces _____ (5) ...
13 ... which is stored in the _____ (7)
14 We do not pass much 12 on _____ days (4) ...
15 ... but we may _____ a lot (5)
16 _____ water is a weak 10 which is always weaker than the 10 inside animals (5)
17 Animals in _____ water are likely to lose water by 7 (3) ...
18 ... so to control this they drink lots of water and then get rid of the _____ from it (4)
19 Inside a plant cell is a _____ which contains fairly strong solution (7)
20 A plant cell which is full is hard and rigid. It is therefore a _____ cell (6)

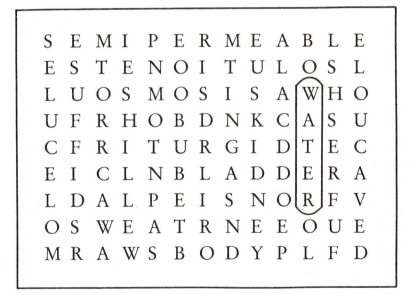

10. Movement in animals

10.1 Bones

Humans have a skeleton made of bones, which support the body and allow it to move. A bone has to be hard to withstand knocks, strong enough not to break or bend and light so that the animal is not too heavy to move. Bones are able to be all these things because they are hollow tubes made of a mixture of living cells and minerals, mostly calcium. Figure 10.1 shows a typical leg bone cut in half along its length to show how it is made. You will be able to see the parts when you look at some real bones.

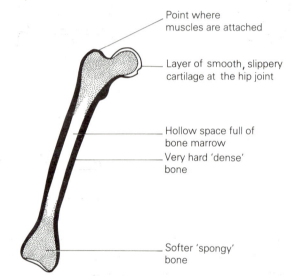

Point where muscles are attached

Layer of smooth, slippery cartilage at the hip joint

Hollow space full of bone marrow

Very hard 'dense' bone

Softer 'spongy' bone

Figure 10.1   A thigh bone cut in half lengthways

Experiment 10.1

Looking at bones

1. Look at a number of bones. Try to find out which part of the skeleton they are from.

2. If necessary, saw the bones up using a hacksaw.

3. Identify marrow, hard compact bone, light spongy bone and cartilage.

4. Place a small length of bone in a boiling tube with some dilute hydrochloric acid (see Figure 10.2). Leave for a few days.

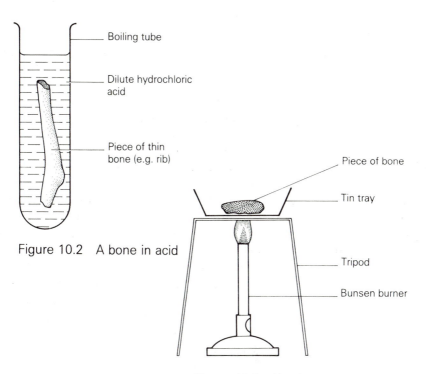

Figure 10.2   A bone in acid

Figure 10.3   Heating a piece of bone

5. Place another small piece of bone on a tin tray on a tripod. Heat the bone strongly with a Bunsen burner from both above and below (see Figure 10.3). Try to burn the bone.

6. After the bone has burnt as much as it can let it cool and then examine it. Can you crush it? Has it any strength? Burning removes the living cells and leaves only the minerals.

7. Examine the bone in acid. Remove it from the acid and rinse it in water. Try bending the bone. The acid dissolves away the minerals and leaves the living organic matter.

8. Describe in your own words what fresh bone is like and what the mineral part and the living organic part are like.

Investigating the strength of bones

HYPOTHESIS: that hollow bones are stronger than solid ones

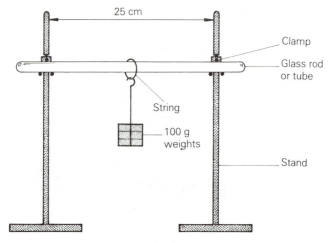

Figure 10.4 Apparatus to compare the strengths of a solid cylinder and a hollow tube

1. You will need safety glasses for this experiment.

2. Cut a 30 cm length of 4 mm diameter glass rod and a 30 cm length of glass tube, choosing the size of tube so that it weighs about the same or just a little less than the rod.

3. Assemble each length of glass on stands as in Figure 10.4 making sure that the clamps are 25 cm apart.

4. Tie a small loop of string around the centre of the rod and the tube.

5. Load weights on to the string steadily increasing the weights until the rod and the tube break.

6. Which could carry more weight, the rod or the tube?

From this experiment you will see that a tube is stronger than a rod, and to get the same strength tubes are much lighter to use than rods. This is why bicycle frames, as well as many other metal structures, are made of tubes.

10.2 The skeleton

Our skeletons are made of an enormous number of bones which are arranged to give us the greatest strength combined with the best movement for the way we live. Not only are the bones themselves hard and strong, but the way they are arranged is very strong too. For example, the bones in the skull are joined together to make a very strong box inside which our brains can be protected. The ribs make a cage which not only moves our chest but protects the lungs and heart inside. (See Figure 10.5.)

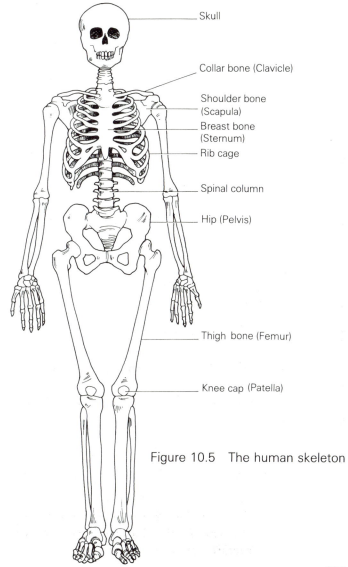

Skull

Collar bone (Clavicle)

Shoulder bone (Scapula)

Breast bone (Sternum)

Rib cage

Spinal column

Hip (Pelvis)

Thigh bone (Femur)

Knee cap (Patella)

Figure 10.5 The human skeleton

1. Trace out Figure 10.6 showing the different parts of the skeleton. The dotted lines will help you when cutting them out.

2. Cut them out and stick them on to another piece of paper so that they make a complete skeleton—Figure 10.5 will help you.

3. Label the main parts of the skeleton.

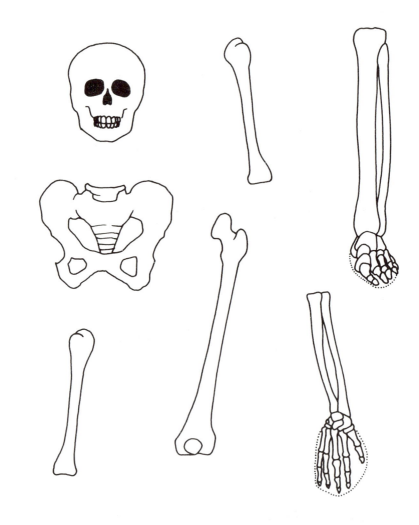

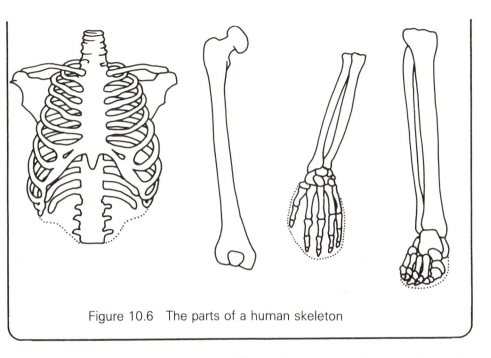

Figure 10.6 The parts of a human skeleton

The human skeleton is different from most other vertebrates because we walk on two legs, leaving our hands free for other jobs. Most vertebrates walk on four legs (see Figure 10.7). It is easier to balance and move with four legs than it is with only two. You can see this in the following simple experiment.

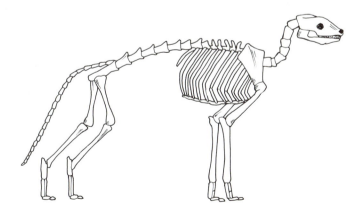

Figure 10.7 The skeleton of a typical mammal

Investigating skeletons

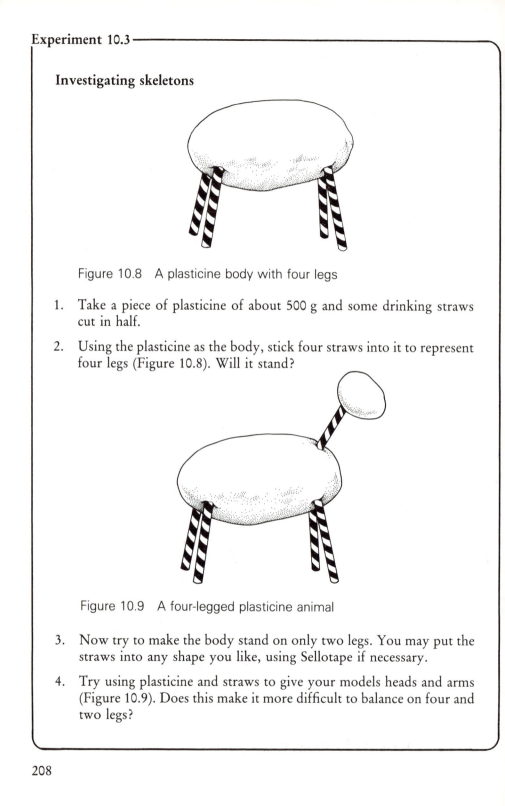

Figure 10.8   A plasticine body with four legs

1. Take a piece of plasticine of about 500 g and some drinking straws cut in half.

2. Using the plasticine as the body, stick four straws into it to represent four legs (Figure 10.8). Will it stand?

Figure 10.9   A four-legged plasticine animal

3. Now try to make the body stand on only two legs. You may put the straws into any shape you like, using Sellotape if necessary.

4. Try using plasticine and straws to give your models heads and arms (Figure 10.9). Does this make it more difficult to balance on four and two legs?

10.3 Joints

Where two bones meet is called a joint and there are three sorts of joints in our skeleton:

(a) The *fixed joint*, which is where the bones are fixed rigidly together. Fixed joints are found in our skulls where the bones have made a strong box to protect the brain.

(b) The *hinge joint*, which allows two bones to move like a hinge. The bones may be joined end to end like in our fingers or knees, or one bone may fit into another as in our elbow.

(c) The *ball-and-socket joint*, which is where one bone has a round end which fits into a round hole in the other bone. We have these in our shoulders and hips, and they allow one bone to swivel around the other.

(See Figure 10.10.)

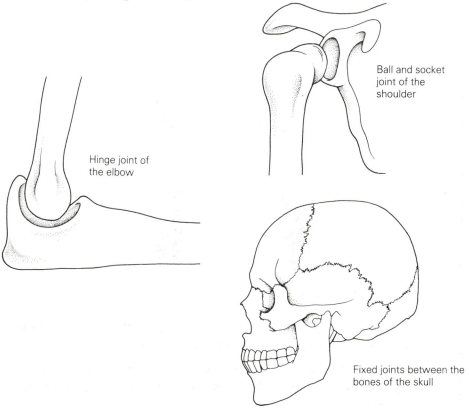

Ball and socket joint of the shoulder

Hinge joint of the elbow

Fixed joints between the bones of the skull

Figure 10.10   Some human joints

The hinge and ball-and-socket joints allow movement because the bones can slide against each other. So that the movement is easy the surfaces of the bones at the joint are covered with *cartilage*—a shiny, slippery substance. To make movement even easier the joint is 'oiled' with a liquid called *synovial fluid*. Finally the whole joint is wrapped in a tough but flexible substance called a *ligament* which stops the bones from becoming separated.

This all produces a joint which is strong and yet moves easily, and where the bones, even though they can move they do not fall apart from each other (see Figure 10.11).

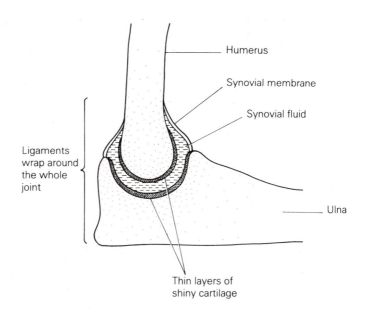

Figure 10.11   The hinge joint of the elbow

Damage to joints

Twisting a joint the wrong way may stretch or tear the ligament and allow the bones to move apart a little. This is called a *sprain* and is cured by holding the bones still by a bandage or with plaster, to give the ligament time to heal. Arthritis is a disease of the joints where they swell up and become very painful. In many cases the joint swells so much that it becomes impossible to move.

10.4 Muscles

You have seen that a skeleton is made of strong bones held together at joints by tough ligaments. By itself, a skeleton like this could not move. It has to have muscles which are attached to the bones and which can pull the bones into different positions. A muscle works only by pulling. To do this the muscle contracts, which means it gets shorter and when it contracts, a muscle can produce a very strong pull. (See Figure 10.12.)

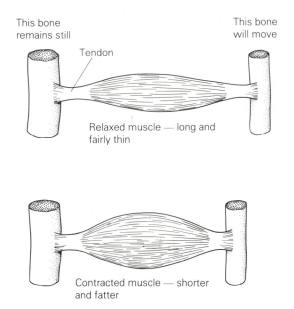

This bone remains still

This bone will move

Tendon

Relaxed muscle — long and fairly thin

Contracted muscle — shorter and fatter

Figure 10.12   A relaxed muscle and a contracted one

In order to move the body the muscles must contract in a very organised way. Certain muscles must contract first, followed by others. This organisation is just one of the functions of the brain which moves our body without us having to think about it. For example, walking: once we have learnt to do it as a baby, it is something we do automatically. If you try to *think* about walking it almost seems to make the movements difficult to do.

You can observe the muscles working in your body by looking at them because a muscle which has contracted becomes fatter and sticks out more. It also becomes very hard as it works and you can feel this hardness by squeezing the muscle. Try the next experiment to see which muscles are involved in simple movements.

Investigating simple movements

1. You can work either in pairs or by yourself. For each action find the muscle or muscles which are involved and write them down. Do not try to find out the muscles' names, just describe where they are.

2. Pick up a fairly heavy weight in your hand and lift it by bending your arm at the elbow.

3. Grip a door handle or ruler or stick hard with your hand.

4. Stand on tiptoe.

5. The next ones are more difficult because you have to move. You should try each movement several times.

6. Do a press-up.

7. Jump up and down on the floor.

8. Stand on one leg and swing the other leg in front of you.

9. Walk.

10.5 Muscles and joints

One of the simplest movements to study is the one described in instruction 2 in Experiment 10.4. This is the movement of the forearm which is raised and lowered by bending at the elbow. In understanding how this movement is brought about you will be able to understand more fully the other movements of the body.

Figure 10.13 shows a model of the bones and muscles involved in this movement. There are two muscles: the *biceps* and the *triceps*. You can feel these in your own arm. The biceps is connected to the shoulder bone and the forearm bone (*ulna*) in front of the elbow. When the biceps contracts, it pulls the forearm up. The triceps is connected to the shoulder blade and the humerus bone, and also to the forearm bone, but this time it is behind the elbow. When the triceps contracts, it pulls the forearm down. You can easily make a model of this movement to see how it works.

A model of the arm muscles

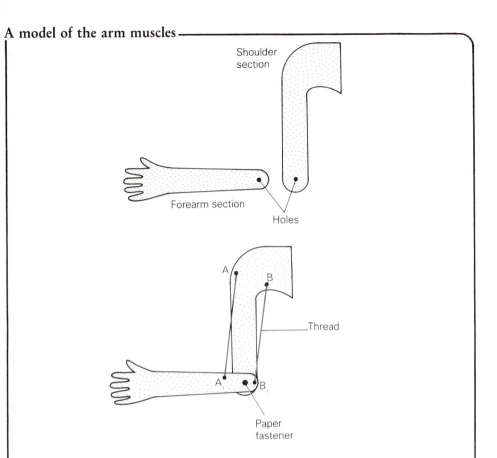

Figure 10.13   A model of the human arm muscles

1. Draw the two shapes on to a piece of stiff card and cut them out.

2. Join the two pieces together by piercing a hole in each and using a paper fastener. Make sure the forearm piece overhangs at the back.

3. Pierce the holes A and A_1 and B and B_1.

4. Take two pieces of string with knots in one end. Thread one piece through hole A_1 and then hole A. Thread the other through hole B_1 and then B.

5. Pulling the string through A and A_1 imitates the action of the biceps. Pulling the string through B and B_1 imitates the action of the triceps.

You can see that a muscle, when it contracts, produces a movement in one direction only. To get the opposite movement you need another muscle. A pair of muscles which give opposite movements is called an *antagonistic pair*. The muscles are said to be *antagonists*. Throughout the body all muscles work in pairs. The biceps and triceps are an antagonistic pair.

Try stretching out your hand then closing it. These are opposite movements caused by pairs of muscles. Can you find which muscles are working?

Tendons Muscles are attached to bone by very strong fibres, which do not stretch at all, called *tendons*. You can find the tendon from your biceps quite easily. If you press the inside of your elbow joint, you will feel the tough tendon, especially if you tense the muscle.

You can see the tendons which work your fingers, too. The muscles which work the fingers are not in the fingers where they would get in the way, but are in the forearm. This allows the fingers to be able to grip objects strongly and do delicate work as well. The muscles are connected to the fingers by long tendons. You can see them, especially on the back of the hand, when you stretch out your fingers and move them.

In the next experiment you can see the tendons in a pig's trotter and by careful dissection you can see how they are connected to bones. You can also see joints and how they work.

Experiment 10.5

Dissecting a pig's trotter

1. Work very carefully in groups. You will have to use sharp scissors and perhaps a very sharp scalpel. Be extremely careful not to cut yourself.

2. Take a pig's trotter (see Figure 10.14). This is the equivalent of your hand except that a pig has only four fingers or toes. Look at the trotter and observe the toes. The trotter will have been cut at the wrist. Observe the very small wrist bones, with their shiny, smooth cartilage surfaces.

3. Carefully cut through the skin down the back of the trotter as in the diagram. The skin is very tough. Work around the trotter to remove as much of the skin as you can.

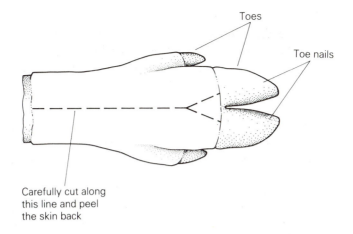

Toes

Toe nails

Carefully cut along
this line and peel
the skin back

Figure 10.14   A pig's trotter

4. Observe the white tendons both on top of and on the underside of the trotter. Try pulling them to see how they move the bones.

5. Trace the tendons to each joint and try to separate them to work each joint independently. How many different tendons are there?

6. Make a clear sketch of the joint from above or below to show the bones and their tendons.

7. Take one of the toe joints. Carefully cut through the ligament around the joint until the bones come apart. Observe how tough and yet flexible the ligament is.

8. With the bones separate, observe the synovial fluid and the cartilage. Put the bones together again to see how easily they move against each other.

9. Make a simple sketch of the joint with the bones slightly apart.

You have now seen that skeletons are made of strong light bones which are held together at joints. Strong fibres called ligaments wrap around the bones at the joints and hold them together. Very tough fibres called tendons join bones to the muscles which work them. Tendons do not stretch so that when the muscles contract they pull the bones. The muscles contract and make the body move.

10.6 Broken bones

Sometimes a bone gets so much force on it that it has to break, or fracture. Figure 10.15 shows an X-ray of a fractured arm. Fractured bones will heal themselves quite easily because the living cells in the bones make more bone to join the parts together at the break. It is important that whilst the bone is healing it is not moved because this would just break it again. Therefore, in most cases, broken bones are held firm in solid cases of plaster so that they cannot move.

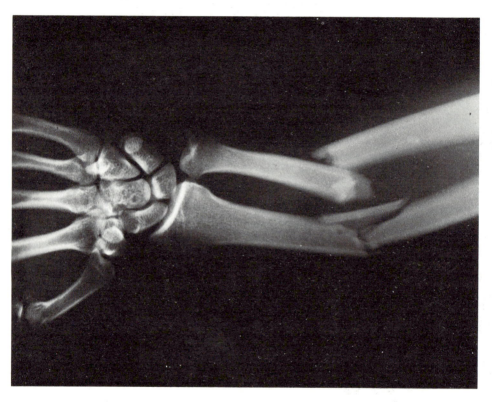

Figure 10.15 An X-ray of a fractured bone

A *green-stick fracture* is a fracture of a bone in a young child. A child's bones are soft while they are still growing and instead of breaking they may bend and crack on one side only, rather like a fresh green twig which will not break cleanly. Because the bones are growing, green-stick fractures often heal much more quickly than fractures in older people.

10.7 Movement in other animals—flying

A bird's wing is shown in Figure 10.16.

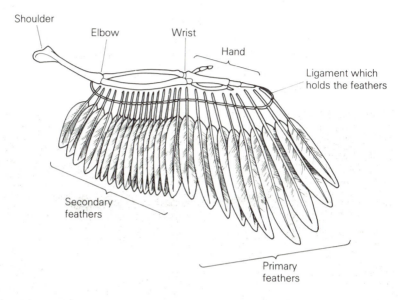

Figure 10.16   A bird's wing

Birds' wings are moved by muscles in the same way that the limbs of other animals are. The flight muscles are very large and powerful and extend across the chest and back of the bird. The most powerful muscles are the ones which pull the wings down, that is, the ones across the chest. When you eat chicken, the breast is the flight muscles, which, even though chickens do not fly, are still very powerful.

The bones of a bird's wing are very similar to the bones of a human arm. A bird has feathers attached to its bones which allow it to push against air and so fly.

Flying is not just a matter of flapping wings up and down. The wings have to have a special shape and the feathers must be arranged to lift the bird up as the wings come down, but not to bring the bird down as the wings go up.

From front to back a bird's wing is shaped like an aerofoil (see Figure 10.17). An aeroplane wing is the same shape, which, because of the way the air flows around it, automatically lifts the bird or the aeroplane up. This shape allows birds like seagulls to soar in the sky only flapping their wings occasionally. In a wing it is the secondary feathers which have this shape.

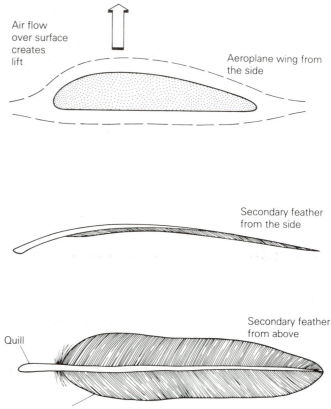

Air flow over surface creates lift

Aeroplane wing from the side

Secondary feather from the side

Quill

Secondary feather from above

Surface of interlocking barbs

Figure 10.17   A bird's feather compared with an aeroplane wing

The primary feathers are arranged so that as the wing is brought down they all close up and push against the air (see Figure 10.18). When the wing goes up the feathers open up and allow the air to pass between them.

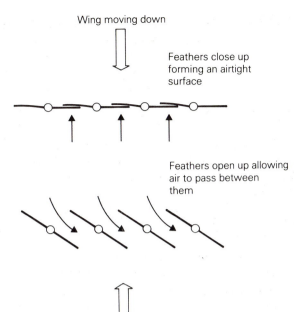

Wing moving down

Feathers close up forming an airtight surface

Feathers open up allowing air to pass between them

Wing moving up

Figure 10.18   The movement of a wing

Experiment 10.6

Looking at feathers

1. Examine a complete bird's wing and compare it with Figure 10.16. Observe the arrangement of primary and secondary feathers.

2. Try moving the wing up and down like a bird would. Can you feel the lift?

3. Take a single feather and look at it closely using a hand lens. Observe how the barbs seem to be held together. Run your finger the 'wrong way' up the feather to pull the barbs apart.

4. Now run your finger back down the feather again. Observe how the barbs seem to lock together again.

5. When a bird preens its feathers, does it do so to unlock the barbs or lock them up again?

10.8 Movement in other animals—swimming

If you observe fish swimming in a tank, you will see that they almost wriggle through the water. This movement is very hard to see since fish move so quickly, and many fish move only the tail end of their body. You can get an idea of the movement in the following simple experiment.

Experiment 10.7

Investigating fish movement

1. Hold your exercise book upright in your hand.

2. Wave it from side to side.

3. Feel the draft that this creates as it pushes the air away. In water this push not only pushes the water away but moves the fish as well.

4. Observe a fish swimming to see if you can see this movement.

The side-to-side movement in fish is caused by the muscles which run down each side. Fish have blocks of muscle on each side which contract first down one side and then down the other. As these muscles contract on one side, they make that side shorter and the fish bends that way. When the other side contracts, the opposite happens. The two sides bending one after the other causes the wriggling movement. (See Figure 10.19.)

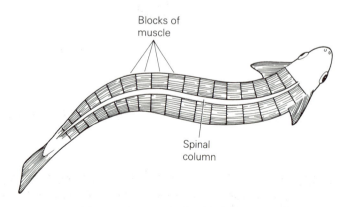

Figure 10.19　The swimming muscles of a fish

When you have a piece of fish for dinner it is these muscles that you eat and you can quite easily see how they are arranged in blocks.

Steering the fish

Only the tail fin is used to push a fish along. The other fins are used to steer the fish and to keep it upright in the water. The upright fins (the *dorsal* and *ventral* fins) stop the fish from rolling around and around and from swaying from side to side (called *yawing*). The horizontal fins (the *pelvic* and *pectoral* fins) stop it from tipping up and down. (See Figure 10.20.)

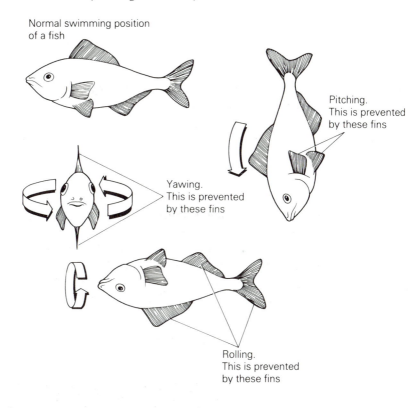

Normal swimming position of a fish

Pitching. This is prevented by these fins

Yawing. This is prevented by these fins

Rolling. This is prevented by these fins

Figure 10.20   The different movements of a fish

Streamlining

A fish is shaped so that it can easily swim through the water. It is said to have a streamlined shape. You can test what difference the shape makes in the next experiment.

221

Investigating streamlining in fish

HYPOTHESIS: that the streamlined shape of a fish allows it to swim more easily in water

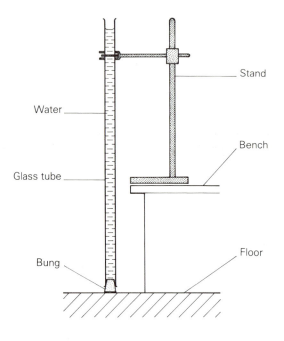

Figure 10.21   Apparatus for investigating streamlining

1. Take a glass tube about two metres long and about 3 cm in diameter with a bung in one end. You will also need a stop-clock and five pieces of plasticine each weighing 10 g.

2. Clamp the tube firmly so that it stands next to the bench with the rubber bung on the floor.

3. Fill the tube almost to the top with water.

4. Make two marks on the tube, one 10 cm from the top and the other 10 cm from the bottom.

5. Take the pieces of plasticine and mould one piece into a cube, one into a triangle. Mould another into a worm shape and one into the shape of a fish. You may make the fifth piece any shape you like.

6. To do the experiment you will have to be very quick. Drop the cube shape into the tube. As it passes the top mark start the stop-clock and stop it as the cube passes the bottom mark. Record the time taken in a results table.

7. Now repeat the experiment for each of the other pieces of plasticine.

8. Do the whole experiment again. To get the plasticine shapes back you must hold the tube over a sink and carefully remove the bung. If you are quick, you may get the plasticine without losing much water.

Shape		Time taken	
	1st run	2nd run	Average

9. Work out the average time for the shapes to fall. Which fell the fastest and which the slowest? Was the hypothesis correct?

10.9 Developing muscles

All sportsmen and women train to develop their skills and their muscles. We are all capable of running or swimming faster than we think; all that is necessary is training. Our muscles work only as hard as they have to, with a little kept in reserve in case some extra is necessary. If you want to run faster or be able to kick or throw a ball further, then you have to train your muscles to work harder. Training builds up the muscles and improves their 'tone'. That means the muscles are more ready to work and instead of being flabby and loose they become tighter. In particular, training improves the most important muscle in the body—the heart. The heart is a pump made of very powerful muscle which forces our blood all around the body, bringing food and essential substances to every part.

It is a good idea to keep all your muscles exercised, because without exercise they quickly stop working so well. When you want to use them, you find that no matter how much you may want to run faster, for instance, your legs just do not seem to do it. This is why all pupils must do sport at school. It helps to make sure that your muscles get exercise.

It is a good idea to continue with a sport after you have left school. It helps to keep your body, and in particular your heart, in good working order. This will allow you to enjoy a longer active life and, as well as improving your muscles, will probably make you feel much better generally.

Questions on Chapter 10

Fill in the spaces in the following sentences.

1. Bones must be _____, _____ and _____.

2. Skeletons are bones jointed together in such a way that they are _____ and yet still allow lots of _____.

3. It is easier for an animal to stand on _____ legs, but having only _____ legs means that there are _____ free for other jobs.

4. A _____ is where two bones meet. The bones are covered in smooth _____ which allows them to slide easily with the help of a liquid called _____. The bones are held together by tough _____ which are able to bend as the bones move.

5. Muscles work by _____ which means they get _____ and _____. Muscles are joined to bones by _____ which are strong and do not _____.

6. Muscles work in pairs called _____ pairs. An example of such a pair is the _____ and _____ muscles in the arm.

7. In children bones may not break cleanly. This is called a _____ fracture.

8. A bird's wing is shaped like an _____ which means that it automatically lifts the bird up as it flies.

9. Fish have a _____ shape and they swim by _____ through the water. This movement is caused by the sets of muscles which run down each _____ of the fish.

10. Name the three sorts of joints in the human skeleton. Make a large labelled diagram of a shoulder joint.

11. Draw the muscle arrangement of the upper arm and explain how the muscles move the arm both up and down.

12. Explain as simply as you can why many of the bones of the skeleton are hollow.

Crossword on Chapter 10

Across

1 Upright ones are called *dorsal* and *ventral* (4)
4 10 across will _____ if too much force is put on it (5)
7 Birds use these to fly (5)
9 A 10 across in the 18 down (4)
10 A hollow tube in the body (4)
11 Word to describe a fracture in a young child's 10 across (10)
13 A 'box' made of bones (5)
15 A fibre which does not stretch (6)
17 Rolling and swaying—some 1 across prevent it (6)
20 12 down help you do this (4)
21, 3 down, 8 down and 12 down. They each have one 10 across with a round end fitting into a round hole in the other 10 across (4, 3, 6, 6)
22 They only work by pulling (7)
23 A swimmer which has 1 across (4)

Down

1 They bend at the knuckles (7)
2 Word meaning 'moves in water' (what a 23 across does) (5)
3 See 21 across
5 12 down between thighs and shins (5)
6 A 23 across doesn't breathe into these (5)
8 See 21 across
10 What is inside 13 across? (5)
12 See 21 across
14 It has a 10 across called a *shin* (3)
16 You have 24 of these bones (4)
18 It has 22 across called the biceps and the triceps (3)
19 Move using 7 across? (3)

Trace this grid on to a piece of paper, and then fill in the answers.

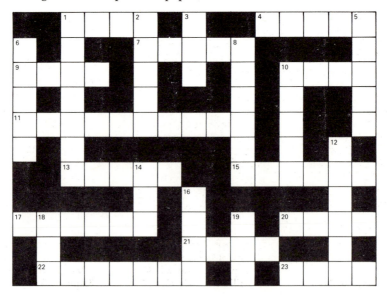

Index